Date Due

PRIMITIVE
TO
PICASSO

ST. PAUL'S SCHOOL ALUMNI COLLECT

ST. PAUL'S SCHOOL
CONCORD, NEW HAMPSHIRE

AN EXHIBITION AT M. KNOEDLER
AND COMPANY
14 EAST 57TH STREET, NEW YORK CITY
2 DECEMBER TO 21 DECEMBER, 1968

LENDERS TO THE EXHIBITION

CATALOGUE EDITOR

Sharon Herson

CATALOGUE ENTRIES

William Barcham   Eunice Loory

Wanda Corn   Charles Moffett, Jr.

Joseph Dye   Cynthia Nachmani

Florence Erb Karasek   Nancy Thompson

Mr. Benjamin Rowland, Jr. has provided entries for works lent from his collection, and Mr. Stuart C. Welch, Jr. has written several of the entries for the Oriental miniatures and has supplied information which was extremely useful for many of the others.

NOTES ON THE CATALOGUE

Dimensions of works are given in inches; height precedes width. The listings of exhibitions have been made available by the owners and are, in many cases, incomplete. Exhibition titles printed in italics refer to the catalogue of the particular show. Authors of catalogues are cited only when the catalogue appears in the bibliography.

ACKNOWLEDGMENTS

This exhibition would not have taken place without the years of devotion to art and St. Paul's School of Mrs. Paul Moore, and the lasting contributions to the School of Arthur A. Houghton, Jr. Among the many alumni who have offered or contributed from their collections and who have so generously taken an active interest, I wish especially to thank Professor Benjamin Rowland, Jr., Professor E. Dudley H. Johnson, Lee A. Ault, James W. Fosburgh, and Stuart C Welch, Jr. for their help and advice. James Biddle has seen this exhibition from the germ of an idea through its initial organization, and John C. Wilmerding, Jr. has had a formative hand in its every aspect. Their assistance in selecting the works of art has been invaluable. Mrs. Colton P. Wagner and Mrs. James Biddle together with Mrs. Moore have planned and organized the benefit. Among those not connected with the School we gratefully appreciate the work on the exhibition in its entirety of Mrs. Charles La Munière and the work of Sharon Herson and William Barcham in preparing the catalogue.

Finally, I wish to thank E. Coe Kerr, Jr., who generously has made this gallery available to us and who has furthered the exhibition in every way, and the Rev. Matthew M. Warren, whose idea it was and whose concern for the arts and education is unique in my experience.

Francis Cunningham

PRIMITIVE TO PICASSO
ST. PAUL'S SCHOOL ALUMNI COLLECT

To see what you are looking at is more complicated than it appears. To hear what you are listening to is more difficult than it sounds. Yet these two skills, seeing and hearing, are essential to us if we are to enter into the experience of art and music. Like drama and the ballet, the arts of painting and sculpture and music will yield their fullest treasures to the initiated, the trained, the conscious seeker.

It is true that the uninitiated and untrained person can derive some satisfaction and pleasure from the arts — this exhibition itself may offer pleasure or discovery in areas with which many of us are unfamiliar. Still it is clear that the rich and varied forms of all the arts reveal themselves best to those who have come to understand what the artist is saying in whatever form the artist chooses.

The Art Department at St. Paul's School, now enjoying the Art Center in Hargate, is engaged in giving our students the initiation, the training, the sensitivity so vital to the life of an educated person. While we are delighted to have a number of distinguished artists among our alumni, our objective in teaching art is not necessarily an attempt to produce practicing artists. Rather, we believe that our graduates, by studio training as well as in courses in the history and theory of art, will appreciate and promote good design and appropriate color and form in all the activities in which their lives and work may involve them.

Many people deny themselves genuine happiness and satisfaction in contemporary art, music, and drama (to say nothing of architecture, or even of the simple pleasure to be derived in light and shadow and darkness falling where they may) by confining their artistic interests to "great" art, "great" music and more traditional forms, colors, and sounds. Our hope is that our graduates will find through their experience in the Art Center in Hargate an openness to new and contemporary art as well as appreciation of all the glories of the artistic wealth of the great and near-great artists of centuries past.

The collection in this catalogue is a tribute to the good taste, training, and sensitivity of our alumni. We aspire to send into the ranks of future alumni hundreds more who will devote their talents and interests to encouraging artistic endeavor wherever it may be found, and will find for themselves the joy of seeing what they are looking at and hearing what they are listening to.

Matthew M. Warren
Rector

Foreword

Anyone who tries to find an appropriate title for a comprehensive exhibition like the present one is tempted by such clichés as "Treasures from Private Collections," "Collectors' Choice," or infinite numbers of variations involving the word "Taste." The present title, *Primitive to Picasso*, was chosen by Francis Cunningham and the writer upon leaving the final meeting for the preparation of this catalogue. After abandoning various combinations of such pretentious labels as "Masterworks" or "Masterpieces," the final choice of *Primitive to Picasso*, for better or worse, is intended to give an idea of the scope of the exhibition from the point of view of taste and time. "St. Paul's School Alumni Collect" remains as a subtitle to indicate the source of the objects and the purpose of the show.

It would of course be impossible to name the influences that fostered the collecting habits of SPS alumni. Many were introduced to an appreciation of the fine arts only through formal instruction at the college level, but certainly formative influences were at work at the School even in the decades before the Second World War. Some of the older graduates were perhaps stimulated by Dr. Drury's infectious discussions of fine books and bindings or the occasional informal instruction in drawing that went on in the 1920s and 1930s. It might have been interesting in this connection to ask each lender what were his first adventures in collecting. For example, the writer would confess to having assembled a collection of Maxfield Parrish reproductions before graduating to Picasso prints. Others in this remote period collected Benson etchings, and a few adventurous souls favored replicas of Cézanne. Undoubtedly, the post-war interest aroused by the teaching of Messrs. Abbe and Higgins has completely changed the place of art at the School from an informal hobby to an important part of the curriculum. It is to benefit and foster the development of the teaching of art and the encouragement of connoisseurship at St. Paul's that this exhibition is dedicated.

We make no pretense of presenting a history of world art in the examples chosen. Some periods and countries are heavily represented, while for other areas there is only a handful of selected works. This disparity is not disturbing; it only demonstrates the taste — diversified or specialized, cosmopolitan or national — that has determined the interest of the collectors. The exhibits are from collections formed in the last half-century, and it is of particular interest, as an indication of the endless attraction of collecting, that many of the finer objects are loaned by recent graduates of St. Paul's. What should attract the connoisseur and the general public is that many of the treasures exhibited have never before been published or shown.

This exhibition has been made possible through the cooperation of a group of alumni who have been happy to share their prized possessions with the public for this occasion. The generous contributions of many sponsors have supported the publication of this catalogue which, it is hoped, will be something more than a souvenir. The collection was assembled by the devotion and hard work of the chairmen: James Biddle, Francis Cunningham, and John Wilmerding.

The exhibition itself includes works of European painting and sculpture with distinguished examples from practically every important period from the prehistoric to the present. It was inevitable that, in a collection of works reflecting so many varied and special tastes, certain areas should be more richly represented than others. It may be noted in this respect that the committee was also fortunate in assembling a splendid selection of American oils and watercolors of the 19th and 20th centuries. Again, with the resources available from a few St. Paul's collectors specializing in Oriental art, it has been possible to mount a strong representation of examples of the art of Iran, India, China, and Japan. This part of the collection ranges from Indian sculpture to Japanese paintings of the Edo period and provides an appropriate balance for the European section.

All of the objects displayed have been selected for their quality as works of art, and reveal the catholic taste and the discerning eye that have led their owners to acquire them. Gertrude Stein once stated that "a little bell rang" whenever she, as a collector, came upon an irresistable work of art. This exhibition demonstrates what made the bell sound for SPS collectors. Some thirty-two alumni have agreed to lend, and it is interesting that no two reflect the same interests in collecting art; some are specialists, some omnivorous. The taste of the lenders, although mainly directed toward the great styles of the past, is by no means conservative or "square," since the loans include abstract forms in primitive and Archaic art as well as in the work of today's avant-garde. The exhibition is calculated to reveal the eye for quality developed by this group of collectors in their life-long devotion to the art of every period and every region of our world.

Benjamin Rowland, Jr.
Harvard University

Primitive Art

PRIMITIVE ART

1.
"BIRD STONE"
U. S. A.; American Indian, date unknown.
Stone; length 6″.

The cultures represented by small stone figurines such as the present example were among the earliest in North America. These "effigy" figurines, produced by prehistoric American Indian tribes, have been found in a belt reaching from the middle Mississippi Valley into eastern Canada.

The delicately shaped head, small eye, and prominent ears may represent a doe or female ungulate, but the rounded body forms are those of a bird. This shape has given rise to the popular name of "bird stone" for objects of this type.

The function of these "effigies" is presently unknown. They were formed by chipping a stone into a rough shape, which was then smoothed and polished with a natural abrasive such as sandstone. Many of these "effigies" were pierced; the small opening seen on this creature's chest may have been formed by a copper or stone drill. A preferred method, however, involved the painstaking use of a rotating stick which impelled the sand, as a cutting agent, into the hard stone. The smooth, expressive contours of this object reveal the expert craftsmanship and sculptural ability of the American Indian tribes who inhabited the eastern area of the present United States and Canada in the prehistoric period.

BIBLIOGRAPHY: Unpublished. General reference: F. H. Douglas and R. D'Harnoncourt, *Indian Art of the United States*, 1941, p. 51.   *Anonymous Loan*

2.

HEAD OF A DIGNITARY

Veracruz; Remojades culture, c.200-600 A.D.
Terracotta; height 10¼″.

This head is an unusually intact fragment belonging to a life-size terracotta votive figure of a type found in the open-pit burials that are typical of the classic Remojades culture of Veracruz. It is believed that the shattered state of these figures was initially caused by ritual smashing or "killing" at the time of offering. The unprotected nature of the pit-burial was also responsible for further damage.

The stark majesty of this piece is emphasized by the strong, smooth planes of the cap, forehead, and cheekbones. These clear surfaces contrast with the deep-set, heavy-lidded eyes. The humanity of the figure is suggested by the slack muscles of the mouth which dominates the softened, recessed area of the lower jaw and chin. The downward curve of the nose provides individuality and unites the opposing qualities of the entire face.

The powerful expression, which is more frequently found in stone, is matched by the technical difficulties involved in the manufacture of large clay figurines. These were thoroughly baked despite the small, low-temperature kilns of the Remojades people.

BIBLIOGRAPHY: A. Emmerich, *Savages Never Carved These Stones*, 1959, p. 54; *Poets and the Past*, ed. by D. Ashton, 1959, p. 38; A. Emmerich, *Art Before Columbus*, 1963, pp. 112-14.

Lent by Mr. and Mrs. Dixon Stanton

3.

FINIAL IN THE FORM OF A BIRD

Colombia; Pre-Columbian, 8th-10th century A.D.
Cast gold; maximum length 6⅜″.

EXHIBITIONS: *The Epstein Collection*, The Arts Council of Great Britain, London, 1960, pl. XII, No. 221.

The gold-manufacturing cultures of pre-Conquest Colombia may be considered the virtual El Dorado of the Spanish conquistadores. The wealth of Colombian gold objects, melted down into ingots by the Spaniards, was equaled only by the high degree of technical and artistic development attained by the Colombian goldsmiths. The variety of styles from the different pre-Conquest cultures of Colombia may be seen today in museums and private collections.

The subject of this exquisite finial, cast by the *cire perdu* process, is probably a toucan; the bird is perched on a gold, cuplike sheath which was once fitted to the top of a bone or wood ceremonial spear (*atl-atl*). Finials of this type were a specialty of the Sinú pre-Conquest culture, whose goldsmiths worked in a semirealistic style enriched with decorative detail. The spiral crest, large eye, and slit pupil are seen on other Sinú bird finials, as are the decorated cere, elaborately rendered beak and delicately modeled body. The small gold rings attached underneath the beak once held gold disks as pendants. The Sinú gold finials exhibit a familiarity with advanced techniques of the jeweler's craft as well as a sensitivity to balanced forms.

BIBLIOGRAPHY: General reference: E. Carli, *Pre-Conquest Goldsmiths' Work of Colombia in the Museo del Oro, Bogota*, 1957 (contains bibliography).

Collection George Ortiz, Geneva

4.
HEAD OF A MAN WITH MASK
Mexico; Toltec, c.10th-12th century A.D.
Stone; height 7¼".

This head is related to the basalt heads now in the British Museum and the National Gallery (Kubler, figs. 18, 19). These heads are believed to represent either the god Xipetotec (Xipe) or his priest who danced at a festival of rejuvenation wearing his "new" covering — provided by the skin of a flayed, human sacrifice. Though the origins of Xipetotec are unclear, it is known that he was a god of the pre-Conquest Mixtec culture, centered at Oaxaca, and the related contemporary Teotihuacan culture. The Toltecs, infiltrating from the north, may have adopted Xipetotec before their rise to power.

The style of these heads was not derived from Mixtec art; it may have been influenced by the less well-known but contemporary "cabecitas colosales" of the Nuiñe region. These were "small" terracotta heads, naturalistic in concept and dull in appearance, the latter due to a flat and rather coarse rendering of the face. The Toltec head's highly complex ear, pierced at the lobe, is also found on the Nuiñe heads, though it is not known whether they, too, represented the god Xipetotec. The use of stone and the refined techniques of the Toltecs lend a monumental quality to this head, despite the unnatural effect caused by the overall simplicity, absence of hair, eyelids, and pupils, and lack of surface contrasts.

BIBLIOGRAPHY: Unpublished. General reference: J. Fernandez, *Coatlique...*, 1959, pp. 236-37; G. Kubler, *The Art and Architecture of Ancient America*, 1962, figs. 18-19; *Ancient Oaxaca*, ed. by J. Paddock, 1966.   *Lent by Mr. Lee A. Ault*

5.
SEATED FIGURE
Ivory Coast; Baole tribe, c.15th century A.D.
Ebony; height 24½".

The reduction of the human form to somewhat distorted, basically geometric components is characteristic of the wood and metal sculpture created by the Ivory Coast tribes of Senoufo, Guro, and Baole. Seated figures are unusual in free-standing wood scultpure of the Baole tribe, but the arched eyebrows, heavy-lidded narrow eyes, flattened nose, and elaborate facial scars are seen on other examples of Baole work. The line of the lengthened, pointed jaw is decorated with the serrated outline of a beard. The figure seems to be stroking or holding the narrow length of this beard which is terminated by a large knob visible below the hand. The body consists of an elongated torso decorated only with a small cicatrix on the chest. The relatively well-shaped arms are unusual in Baole sculpture which generally shows thin, almost rudimentary arms held close to the body and summarily rendered. The heavy legs with thick ankles and the small buttocks are found on all Baole figurines. This work is an extremely fine example of Baole wood sculpture. The carefully finished surface and subdued lines lend a harmonious, smooth movement to the dignified figure whose visage commands attention and respect.

BIBLIOGRAPHY: Unpublished. General reference: E. Elisofon, *La Sculpture africaine* (text by W. Fagg), 1958, pp. 94-104.   *Lent by Mr. Lee A. Ault*

6.

HEAD

Nigeria; "South Niger," c.17th century A.D.
Bronze, brown patina; height 9″.

This head is characterized by extreme stylization. The short, rounded curve of the forehead and jutting profile of the nose are offset by the thick protruding lips and elongated jaw. The large bulging eye is rimmed by narrow incised lids and underlined by the high plane of the upper cheek. The wide nose is terminated abruptly by a straight indentation from nostril to nostril. The highly decorative treatment of the hair, ears, and facial scars lends a fine and imaginative aspect to the otherwise heavy but forceful features. The rendering of this hollow head indicates a close relationship with heads from tribes of the so-called South Niger complex; these tribes were culturally affiliated with the well-known tribes of Benin and Ife. Although this group of heads differs markedly from the delicate, naturalistic portraits of the Ife, their dynamic quality may have had a special significance to their creators. Several heads of this type seem to have served as "altar" attachments. However, the owner believes that this piece may have been used as a bell, although the clapper and its attachment are now missing.

BIBLIOGRAPHY: Unpublished. General reference: E. Elisofon, *La Sculpture africaine* (text by W. Fagg), 1958, pp. 120-31; W. Fagg, *Nigerian Images*, 1963.

Collection George Ortiz, Geneva.

7.

RELIQUARY HEAD

Africa; Bakota tribe, 19th century A.D.
Copper, brass, and wood; height 16″.

The abstract treatment of this image is in the tradition of the Bakota tribe; its reliquary figurines are characterized by large, flat heads — usually sheets of hammered brass or copper over wood. The head is supported by a tall, cylindrical neck attached to an upright, diamond-shaped open base. The base, which is probably a symbolic representation of the human body, and the wooden neck are also covered with sheets or plaques of brass or copper. The rendering of this image is determined by a pre-established form in which variations are limited to differences in the facial features and minor alterations within the set pattern of the head. The purpose of the Bakota figurine is to protect the bones of the dead chief or dignitary placed within the reliquary case.

BIBLIOGRAPHY: E. Elisofon, *La Sculpture africaine* (text by W. Fagg), 1958, p. 183, Nos. 224-28

Lent by Mr. Paul M. Ingersoll

Ancient Art

ANCIENT ART

8.

SEATED MONKEY
Iran (found near Susa) ; proto-Elamite, early 3rd millennium B.C.
Alabaster; height 3¾".

EXHIBITIONS: *Ancient Art in American Private Collections,* Fogg Art Museum, Cambridge, Mass., 1954-55, No. 56.

The depiction of animals engaged in human activities is a frequent theme in ancient Elamite and Mesopotamian art of the early 3rd millennium B.C. This seated monkey drinks from a long cup which he holds with both front paws. He sits on a flat, almost circular base which contains a round indentation for the placement of a cup or bowl. He possesses an appealing *insouciance* despite the rather summary rendering of form and detail. This small figurine is related to a number of similar statuettes found at the proto-Elamite center of Susa in southwestern Iran.

BIBLIOGRAPHY: General reference: *Mémoires de la delegation en Perse,* XIII, 1912, pl. XXXIX: 5, 7; L. Le Breton, "The Early Periods at Susa," *Iraq,* XIX (1957) p. 111, figs. 32, 37; E. Strommenger, *Art of Mesopotamia,* 1964, figs. 34-37; P. Amiet, *Elam,* 1966, pp. 114-16; E. Porada, *The Art of Ancient Iran,* 1966, pp. 35-37. *Lent by Mr. Stuart C. Welch, Jr.*

9.

MARE ON SOLID BASE (FOAL MISSING)
Greece; Geometric, 8th century B.C.
Cast and solid bronze, dark olive-green patina; height 3¾".

The small bronze group comprising mare and foal was a frequent theme in Geometric bronze sculpture of the Peloponnesos. Many of these groups have been found at the major religious centers of Olympia in Elis, the sanctuary of Artemis Orthia at Sparta in Laconia, and the Athenian Acropolis, where they were probably deposited as votive offerings.

The attribution of a particular style to a specific city or locality is still a subject of study. This mare shows the attenuated legs, narrow cylindrical rib-cage, thickened foreleg, and rounded substantial haunch which are considered characteristic of the Laconian style. Statuettes in this style have been found at both Sparta and Olympia. The lengthened, finely modeled head with realistically shaped foreface, small rounded ear, and barely discernible mane are also typical of Peloponnesian works ascribed to the mid-8th century B.C.

The tail of this mare, once perpendicular to the body and attached to the base, has been broken and bent inward. Despite this injury and the loss of the foal, the expression and rendering create an impressive example of Greek artistry in the Geometric period.

The underside of the solid base bears an incised design that may have been used as a seal.

BIBLIOGRAPHY: Unpublished. General reference: A. Furtwängler, *Olympia,* IV, 1890, pl. 14, Nos. 217, 219; R. M. Dawkins, *The Sanctuary of Artemis Orthia at Sparta,* 1929; E. Kunze, *et al., Olympia Berichte,* IV, VII; N.Himmelman-Wildschutz, *Bemerkungen zur geometrischen Plastik,* 1964. *Collection George Ortiz, Geneva*

10.
FIBULA
Turkey; Lydian or Phrygian, 8th-7th century B.C.
Electrum; length including chain 3½".

The widespread popularity of the fibula (safety pin) in the ancient world is shown by the many variations in the structure and decoration of this useful object. This particular two-piece type seems to have been a specialty of Asia Minor; it is found at the Phrygian site of Gordion and at Ephesos on the coast of Lydia, where fibulae were used as dedicatory offerings and for practical purposes.

The upper part consists of a semicircular arc, round in section and decorated at regularly spaced intervals with molded disks. The rectangular guardplate of the lower part is removable; it is decorated with a design surrounded by bosses and serves to conceal the two parallel, straight pins which are attached to a deeply grooved "double disk." The latter is located under the volute at one end of the arc. At the opposite end, the concealed pins are held in place by a T-shaped catch with raised edges on two sides and a raised strip down the middle. A quadruple chain that terminates in a molded disk and the four single chains ending in small globules are additional ornaments.

Although this type of fibula is often called Phrygian, electrum examples such as the one shown here are absent from the bronze remains at Gordion. On the other hand, the Lydian site of Ephesos has produced several electrum and bronze versions of the type, as well as electrum chains and globules. The use of this form in both Phrygia and Lydia appears to have coincided circa late 8th-7th century B.C.

BIBLIOGRAPHY: Unpublished. General reference: D. G. Hogarth, *Ephesos*, 1920, pl. IV:29, pl. VI:3, pl. VII:30, 32; C. Blinkenberg, *Fibules grecques et orientales*, 1926, pp. 222-24; R. S. Young, "The Gordion Campaign of 1957," *AJA*, 62 (1958) p. 152; ———, "Bronzes from Gordion's Royal Tomb," *Archaeology*, 11 (1958) pp. 228-30; O. W. Muscarella, "Ancient Safety Pins," *Expedition*, 6 (1963-64) pp. 34-40.   *Lent by Mr. Stuart C. Welch, Jr.*

11.
PLAQUE IN THE FORM OF A PANTHER OR LIONESS
U.S.S.R.; Scythian, 7th-6th century B.C.
Cast bronze; length 7¼".

This piece seems to be a mirror image of the cast bronze "lioness" plaque from Siberia, now in the Hermitage. Both plaques are relatively simple examples of the "Scytho-Siberian animal style," which differs somewhat from the Scythian style of the South Russian and Kuban areas. Both "lionesses" or "panthers" are probably earlier in date than the highly complex "animal combat" plaques to which they are stylistically related.

The elongated animal is seen as a semicircle; the clear curve of the lengthened neck and body is broken at symmetrical intervals by the circular, slightly raised forms of the head, shoulder, and haunch. This decorative, highly unnatural attenuation of the body emphasizes the lithe, dramatic quality of the leonine beast. The open area within the arc formed by the body is filled with the drooping tail and legs held in a springing position. The profile view of the animal is underscored by the depiction of only two legs, rather than four. Each part of the body is connected by a short, narrow metal rod.

Although this piece may reflect native Siberian tradition, South Russian Scythian features are already present in the form of the head and the shapes of the ear, square muzzle, and open mouth. Near Eastern, presumably Achaemenid, influence is shown by the presence of indentations and circles for inlays.

BIBLIOGRAPHY: E. Minns, *Scythians and Greeks*, 1913 (2nd ed., 1965), p. 274, fig. 194; G. Borovka, *Scythian Art*, 1928, pl. 45; *Catalogue of the fine collection of important early Chinese bronzes, rare archaic jades, ceramics, and works of art: the property of H. K. Burnet, Esq.*, Sotheby and Co., London, April 2-4, 1941, lot 362, pl. facing p. 89; S. Piggott, *Ancient Europe*, 1965, pl. 26.   *Lent by Mr. Stuart C. Welch, Jr.*

12.
YOUTH IN HELMET AND BOOTS
Greece (allegedly from Olympia) ; Peloponnesian workshop, c.520 B.C.
Bronze, green patina with red traces; height 7¾″.

EXHIBITIONS: *Meisterwerke griechischer Kunst*, Kunsthalle, Basel, June 18-Sept. 13, 1960, pp. 34, 181, No. 173; *Master Bronzes from the Classical World*, Fogg Art Museum, City Art Museum of St. Louis, Los Angeles County Museum of Art, 1967-68, p. 55, No. 38.

This vigorous, confident youth stands on a rectangular plinth with holes at diagonally opposite corners. He may have held a lance in his perforated right fist and a shield in his left hand. On the basis of general type (armed warrior) and physical characteristics such as the elongated thighs, oval face, and sharply delineated features, the youth has been attributed to a Laconian workshop (see bibliography). There are, however, several factors which distinguish this carefully modeled figure from Laconian works of the same period and suggest that its origin in a city of the northeast Peloponnesos is perhaps more likely. The laced shoes and the helmet worn by this youth differ from the higher boots and Corinthian helmets worn by Spartan figures. The rather rare helmet type shown here is similar to those worn by Attic figures of Athene (see *Meisterwerke*, p. 34). Also, the long torso, evenly balanced proportions, and comparatively relaxed stance depart from Laconian examples. Still more important differences are seen in the modeling of the abdomen, the unusual groove from navel to pubis, the linear outline of the pubic area, and the light incision depicting body hair. All these features are evident on a somewhat later seated male figure, presumably from Corinth. Despite the debate concerning its origin, the youth remains an unusually fine example of late Archaic bronze sculpture.

BIBLIOGRAPHY: J. Charbonneux, *Les bronzes grecs*, 1958, pp. 69, 141, pl. VIII:1.   *Collection George Ortiz, Geneva*

13.
STANDING DISKOPHOROS
Greece; Graeco-Roman copy of a work by Naukydes (c.400 B.C.)
Marble; height 16″.

Although some scholars believe that there were two sculptors named Naukydes, it seems likely, on the authority of Pliny, that there was only one master with this name—the son of Patrokles, brother of the famous Polykleitos. This argument would seem to be supported by the style of this statue, which, in its softer treatment of the body, betrays only a lingering reminiscence of the hard, block-like manner of Polykleitos himself. The statue appears to represent the last phase of the Polykeitan model. It is a reduced mirror image of other copies of the famous original and was presumably made in the time of Augustus.

BIBLIOGRAPHY: For other versions of the subject, see: *Enciclopedia dell'Arte antica e orientale*, V, 1963, figs. 489-90.   *Lent by Mr. Benjamin Rowland, Jr.*

14.
PLATE WITH RELIEF MEDALLION
Greece (found at Galaxidi, near Delphi) ; Corinthian, c.360 B.C.
Bronze, olive-black patina; diameter 9″.

EXHIBITIONS: *Meisterwerke griechischer Kunst*, Kunsthalle, Basel, June 18-Sept. 13, 1960, pp. 88-89, 261, No. 319.

The owner considers this plate a rare example of 4th century B.C. Corinthian metalwork. The central medallion, which bears a frontally facing head in relief, is said to have been made separately and soldered to the plate with lead. This method of attachment for cold-worked bronze is extremely unusual on Greek objects. It has been observed that this head also differs in technique from the repoussé heads more frequently found on late 5th-4th century B.C. mirror covers. The head has been interpreted as a representation of a disheveled maenad with lips parted and eyes widened in excitement. Similar heads often occur on vases and coins of the same period and later, while the pearl decoration below the molding on the circumference of the plate is also prevalent on contemporary coins. The plate may have been an offering from a treasury at Delphi.

Collection George Ortiz, Geneva

15.
FEMALE HEAD
Greece; 4th century B.C.
Marble; height 8″.

Several characteristics of this fragmentary head suggest that it once belonged to a Greek grave stele. The calm, introspective expression, the slight asymmetry of the features, and the rendering of the head in high relief recall the heads of seated or standing women on Attic grave steles of the 4th century B.C. Although the veil is now lost, the lines traced by this traditonal garb of the deceased or mourning Greek woman are visible behind the three-banded fillet worn toward the front of the head. The missing veil would have covered part of the woman's left ear which remains in a relatively unfinished state. The fragment that adheres to her right cheek may have belonged to the other side of the veil; the latter would have formed part of the background against which the face and head were placed. This fragment, as well as the flattened form of the right cheek, the direction of the glance, and the curve of the fillet around the forehead together suggest that the head was intended to be seen in a semi-profile view facing toward the figure's right.

Despite the fragmentary condition of this head, enough remains to suggest its approximate date. A similar arrangement of hair and fillet is seen on the seated figure of the Attic woman Hegeso whose stele, dated c.400 B.C., is now in the Athens National Museum. The somewhat florid features, however, speak for a later, 4th century, date. The style is reminiscent of a softened and modified Praxitelean manner.

BIBLIOGRAPHY: Unpublished. General reference: F. Johansen, *The Attic Grave Reliefs*, 1951; R. Lullies and M. Hirmer, *Greek Sculpture*, 1957.
Anonymous Loan

16.
IBIS
Egypt; Ptolemaic, c.300 B.C.
Wood with bronze legs; length 6¼″.

As a result of constant warfare, conquest by Alexander the Great, and subsequent occupation by the

Ptolemies in the last half of the 1st millennium B.C., the ancient traditions of Egypt were altered in form and purpose. Despite these changes, established artistic techniques and religious practices persisted under Ptolemaic rule.

This small wooden ibis reflects the continuation of the Egyptian craftsman's sensitivity to substance and line, but the stylization of earlier periods has by this time given way to increasingly naturalistic forms. The sure modeling of the bill and head becomes somewhat coarsened in the heavy body; the silhouette, however, is still characterized by fluidity and balance. A part of the painted gesso surface that once covered the body remains at the rear. It shows incised, painted feathers rendered in a highly decorative and elaborate pattern.

The ibis, as the sacred bird of the ancient god Thoth, was often used as a votive offering. Mummified bodies of ibises, as well as effigies in wood or bronze, have been found in temples and sanctuaries. The frequency of these offerings in the Ptolemaic period perhaps testifies to the important role of Thoth in the popular Osiris cult which flourished at that time.

BIBLIOGRAPHY: Unpublished. General reference: G. Roeder, *Ägyptische Bronzewerke*, 1937, pp. 62-64, taf. 37; J. H. Breasted, *The Development of Religion and Thought in Ancient Egypt*, 3rd ed., 1959, *passim*; W. S. Smith, *Ancient Egypt*, 1960, pp. 154-202.

Anonymous Loan

17.

PLATE WITH "GODDESS ANAHITA"

Iran; Sasanian, 5th-6th century A.D.
Silver with mercury gilding; diameter 8″.

The nude or thinly clad voluptuous female figure is a recurrent theme in Sasanian and post-Sasanian metalwork. This lady is usually depicted with animals and birds or shown with the king in banquet and "investiture" scenes. She has often been called a "dancing girl" or queen, but there is some reason to believe that Sasanian examples may represent either the goddess Anahita or her priestess.

The *repoussé* figure on this plate is shown in low relief. However, her head, in high relief, was worked separately and applied to the inner plate with solder. Also in repoussé is the long semicircular scarf which the "goddess" holds above her head. Her pose is reminiscent of nude goddesses in earlier Near Eastern art. A further indication of divinity or rank is the complex headdress surmounted by a hairball, or "topknot," also found on the crowns of Sasanian kings. The rosette on the headdress and the two elaborately engraved pheasants flanking the figure are also considered attributes of the goddess Anahita. The highly stylized and complicated feather pattern is unusual in Sasanian work, but a less elaborate pheasant with identical head treatment is shown on the base of a Sasanian silver bowl.

Mercury gilding lends color and contrast to this plate, but its practical purpose as a cover for surface joins was not overlooked by Sasanian craftsmen. For technical and stylistic reasons, this plate may be assigned to the 5th-6th century A.D.

BIBLIOGRAPHY: Unpublished. General reference: R. Ghirshman, *Persian Art . . .*, 1962, pp. 119-253; E. Porada, *The Art of Ancient Iran*, 1965, pp. 192-225 and notes, pp. 266-67; R. Ettinghausen, "A Persian Treasure," *Arts in Virginia*, 8 (1967-68) pp. 29-41.

Lent by Mr. Stuart C. Welch, Jr.

European Art

18.

PAIR OF ELIZABETHAN TANKARDS*
Silver-gilt, weight 43 ounces; height 8¼″.
Marked: London, 1602.

Silver tankards, which were quite popular in England during the 17th century, do not appear to have been made prior to the 16th century. Those of the late Elizabethan and early Jacobean periods are marked by a slight tapering in the outline of the shape. The horizontal banding, which divides the form into several sections, creates an impression of size and weight greater than those of the actual object. The banding also enabled the craftsman to vary the surface patterning, contrasting the deep relief of the thick moldings with the surface embossing of the florid "strapwork" motif. This motif itself comes from the first School of Fontainebleau, France (c.1530-50), and was used frequently in European tankard design.

A silver tankard similar in size, shape, and design to this uncommon pair is reproduced in Jackson (see Jackson, fig. 984).

*Only one is illustrated.
BIBLIOGRAPHY: C. J. Jackson, *An Illustrated History of English Plate*, II, 1911.   *Lent by Mr. Arthur A. Houghton, Jr.*

19.
CERES
DANESE CATTANEO (Italian), c.1509-1573.
Bronze; height 13″.

Cattaneo was a student of Jacopo Sansovino, the most important sculptor in Venice in the mid-16th century. Although Tuscan by birth (born in Carrara), Cattaneo spent the greatest number of his active years outside Florence, first in Rome and then in Venice, working alongside his teacher. His principal work is the Fregoso altar in S. Anastasia, Verona, finished in 1565.

This figure of Ceres, the Roman corn-goddess, reveals the fluidity of outline, the long but thick proportions, and the kind of graceful pose that typify Cattaneo's work. The mannered elegance common to both Italian painting and sculpture of the second half of the 16th century is embodied here. The slightly bent right knee, the rather quiet turn of the head, and the slow movement of the arms as they touch the body convey a sense of self-conscious grace that accurately represents the attitudes of a highly sophisticated courtly society.

BIBLIOGRAPHY: General reference: J. Pope-Hennessy, *Italian High Renaissance and Baroque Sculpture*, 1963; A. Venturi, *Storia dell'arte italiana*; 1937, X-iii, pp. 1-35.   *Anonymous Loan*

20.
VULCAN
ANONYMOUS (Italian), 16th century.
Bronze; height 10½″ (without base).

This work depicts Vulcan, the Roman smith-god, hammering at his forge. His characteristic lameness is shown by the unusual iconographic device of a wooden leg. The stance of the figure is related in a general way to the type of contorted body executed by Michelangelo in his *Slaves*, now in the Accademia in Florence. But the energy and muscular strain so evident in those early 16th-century works are missing here. In the *Vulcan* the emphasis is on outlining a pose rather than on depicting a body twisting violently in space. There is, however, great activity in the light which plays over the rippling muscles of the body.

Anonymous Loan

21.
CROUCHING APHRODITE
FRANCESCO SUSINI (Italian) ?-1646.
Bronze; height 8½″.

Francecso Susini was the nephew and student of Antonio Susini, a collaborator and follower of Giovanni da Bologna. The latter, a Fleming who settled in Italy about 1554, was the most prominent Mannerist sculptor in Florence in the second half of the 16th century. Giambologna produced many small bronze works which are characterized by attenuated proportions, elegantly smooth surfaces, and poses that are at once artificial and graceful. Susini's predilection for this style, combined with his interest in small bronzes, reflects his Giambologna heritage. This kind of antique subject, moreover, reveals the late 16th- and 17th-century taste for ancient sculpture. This figure, in fact, is derived from an Aphrodite type popular in Hellenistic sculpture. While the Greek sculptor often emphasized realistic details such as the fleshiness of the stomach, Susini concentrated on producing extremely smooth surfaces which show almost no wrinkle or muscular crease. As a result, broad patches of light are reflected upon the bronze surface, thereby contributing to the feeling of preciousness in this piece.

Anonymous Loan

22.
ICON: THE EUCHARIST
Russia; Novgorod (?), 16th century.
Panel; 23 x 21¼".

The Russian icon is essentially a liturgical object and was painted primarily for purposes of prayer, meditation, and religious instruction. Although artistic considerations were often not of prime importance, they were not entirely ignored; in the presence of a beautiful image, the worshiper would more likely submit himself to its otherwordly vision and religious dictates. The pure, brilliant colors of the icon and its gold background would have flashed in the dark church while candles flickered before the iconostasis (the screen that separates nave from sanctuary in the Orthodox church) on which the icon was placed.

This particular work, executed at about the time when the Russian icon had reached its artistic heights, shows an insistence upon linear patterning. The movement from right to left of the hems of the robes and undergarments is accentuated by a corresponding increase in distance between the figures as they move toward Christ. The emphasis on His divinity is further stressed by His complete separateness from His human disciples. His halo, the liturgical canopy overhead, and the altar before which He offers communion to His apostles also aid in communicating Christ's divine nature.

BIBLIOGRAPHY: L. Ouspensky and V. Lossky, *The Meaning of Icons*, 1952, p. 66;
W. M. Conway, R. Fry, *et al.*, *Masterpieces of Russian Painting*.   *Lent by Mr. Stuart C. Welch, Jr.*

23.
ST. GEORGE
"VICINO DA FERRARA" (Italian), active c.1480.
Oil on panel; 32½ x 12½".

The *St. George* is a superb example of the work of "Vicino da Ferrara," an artistic personality identified and named by Roberto Longhi. The style of the *St. George* closely follows those of Ercole de'Roberti and Francesco del Cossa, the leading Ferrarese artists of the second half of the 15th century. The outline and the position of the figure in relation to the picture plane are, in fact, particularly close to Ercole's own *St. George*, (Longhi, pl. 305), once part of the Griffoni altarpiece (dated c.1470-73). The painting is a striking combination of masculine fortitude and courtly grace, qualities often found together in 15th-century Italian art. The rigid pose, the forthright glance of the eyes, and the massive armour provide strong relief for the tiny feet, the modish hat, and the *au courant* coiffure. St. George's halo, however, seems rather *retardataire* as it sits behind the strikingly realistic face. A delicate shadow only slightly veils the face as the figure poses in a niche. The earthbound quality of the figure is balanced by the buoyant fluid patterning of the unfurled banner.

BIBLIOGRAPHY: M. Meiss, *Burlington Magazine*, XCIII (1951) pp. 69-72;
R. Longhi, *Officina Ferrarese*, 1956, pp. 137-38, pl. 323.   *Lent by Mr. and Mrs. James Biddle*

24.
REARING HORSE
GIOVANNI STRADANUS (Jan van der Straet, Italo-Flemish), 1523-1605.
Pencil on paper; 12⅞ x 14⅛".

Stradanus was a member of the circle of Giorgio Vasari and assisted him in many of the frescoes in the Palazzo Vecchio. He is known by a series of prints of equine subjects, including the set engraved by Collaert in 1594, *Equi Ioannis Austriaci Caroli V*. A number of drawings similar to the present example exist in the collection of the Uffizi in Florence (Paolo Barocchi, *Mostra di disegni di Giorgio Vasari e la sua cerchia*, Gabinetto disegni e stampe degli Uffizi, XVII, 1964, Nos. 92-93).

Lent by Mr. Benjamin Rowland, Jr.

25.
PERSEUS AND ANDROMEDA
CONDE DON FRANCISCO DIAZ DE LA REGUERA (Spanish), 16th century.
Tempera on vellum; 10½ x 7¼″ (15 x 11¾″ with frame).

The identity of the master of this miniature is a complete mystery. The style and tonality of the picture are closely related to works of the masters who decorated the Studiolo of Francesco I dei Medici in the 1570s. In this connection, it may be noted that the pose of Andromeda is derived from Giovanni da Bologna's *Apollo*, which actually adorns the Studiolo, and the figure of Perseus diving toward the sea monster is adapted from the same artist's famous bronze of *Mercury*. The signature, in gold in a small escutcheon at the bottom of the miniature, reads "Con(de) Don Fran(ci)sco Diaz de la Reguera faciebat."

The ivory plaques inlaid in the ebony frame relate the story of Perseus. The frame, presumably contemporary with the miniature, is an international type found in 16th-century Spain, as well as in Italy and northern Europe.

Lent by Mr. Benjamin Rowland, Jr.

26.
PRINCESS SIBYLLE OF CLEVES
LUCAS CRANACH (German), 1472-1553.
Oil on panel; 20¾ x 15″.

This portrait of Sibylle, Princess of Cleves (1512-54) was probably painted to celebrate her engagement in 1526 or her marriage the following year to John Frederick the Magnanimous of Saxony. Another version exists in Weimar (see Ruhmer, pl. 19), along with a pendant work depicting the bridegroom John Frederick.

The painting shows Cranach's mature portrait style. The subject is placed against a flat, neutral background which dissociates her from everyday reality. The cold, bright light spread evenly over the entire figure and the special attention paid to each tiny detail emphasizes those external features which declare the sitter's rank and station.

BIBLIOGRAPHY: M. J. Friedlaender and J. Rosenberg, *Die Gemälde von Lucas Cranach*, 1932; E. Ruhmer, *Cranach*, 1963.

Lent by Mr. Arthur A. Houghton, Jr.

27.
PORTRAIT OF FRANCIS I
JOOS VAN CLEVE (Flemish), c.1485-1540/41.
Oil on panel; 6½ x 5½″.

EXHIBITIONS: *Le portrait dans l'art flamand de Memling à Van Dyck*, Orangerie des Tuileries, Paris, 1952-53, No. 5

Joos van Cleve, or van Cleef, was a Netherlandish painter who became an Antwerp master in 1511.

In 1530, he traveled to the French court of Francis I and painted several portraits of the king and his wife, Queen Eleanor. The attribution of this particular portrait of Francis moved back and forth for years between Jean Clouet and Joos van Cleve. However, it has been attributed to the latter by such authorities as Friedlaender (see bibliography) and Charles Sterling (Frick Art Reference Library, 1942).

Van Cleve was not a great inovator, and the historian looks in vain for artistic experiments within his work. The format in this painting follows that of the standard Renaissance portrait-bust. However, the abstract arrangement of forms — such as the placement of white in feather, collar, and bodice — and the realism of texture and facial expression combine to create a memorable portrait of the French ruler.

BIBLIOGRAPHY: M. J. Friedlaender, *Die Altniederlandische Malerei*, 1931, IX, p. 139, No. 72e.

Lent by Mr. Arthur A. Houghton, Jr.

28.
THE HORSE-TAMERS OF MONTECAVALLO
MARTEN VAN HEEMSKERCK (Dutch), 1498-1574.
Pen, bistre ink on paper; 9⅜ x 9⅞".

Marten van Heemskerck, one of many Dutch artists to seek his fortune in Rome in the 16th century, is best known for drawings of the antiquities of Rome in sketch books formerly preserved in the Kupferstih-Kabinett in Berlin. This drawing is typical of Heemskerck's hatching technique, whereby in a strange way the sculptured images appear more like living effigies than plastic counterparts. On the reverse side of the drawing is a sketch of an unidentified spiral staircase.

BIBLIOGRAPHY: B. Rowland, Jr., "Montecavallo Revisited," *The Art Quarterly*, XXX, 2 (1967) fig. 2.

Lent by Mr. Benjamin Rowland, Jr.

29.
SKULL
HERCULES SEGHERS (Dutch), c.1589-1635/38?
Oil; 10¼" x 11⅞".

EXHIBITIONS: The Mauritshuis, The Hague, 1967-68.

Hercules Seghers is perhaps best known for his visionary paintings and etchings of wild, often mountainous terrain. This work — an uncommon subject for the artist — is probably his painting of a skull bequeathed to the Amsterdam Surgeon's Guild in 1663, a picture which was sold at auction as a Rembrandt in 1853 for the benefit of the Guild's widows' fund. Although the painting is topographically accurate enough to satisfy an anatomist, it transcends the more conventional naturalism associated with contemporary Dutch still-life painting, as represented by the many examples of skulls in *vanitas* pictures. Like Seghers' etched skull, with which it invites comparison both in anatomy and mood, the motif is simultaneously macabre and suggestive of livelier forms. Looked at in detail, the painting—like all of Seghers' work whatever the outward subject—evokes a fantastic landscape, an inviting realm of grottoes, pinnacles, and fields.

Anonymous Loan

30.

PROFILE HEAD OF A WOMAN (PROCRIS?)

THE FLORA MASTER (French), School of Fontainebleau, active c.1540-1560.
Tempera on panel; 19½ x 16¼″.

EXHIBITIONS: *Between Renaissance and Baroque, European Art 1520-1600*, City of Manchester Art Gallery, Manchester, 1965, No. 103.

The profile is rather close to the head of a figure in a drawing in the Germain Seligman Collection, New York, representing the *Death of Procris*. (This drawing is reproduced in *Van Clouet tot Matisse*, 1958, p. 11, p. 8, and mentioned by Sylvie Béguin, *L'Ecole de Fontainebleau*, 1960, p. 73 and n. 60.) The Flora Master is named after the painting of Flora, formerly in the collection of Baron d'Albenas, Montpellier. This artist has been tentatively identified by Mme. Béguin as Ruggiero dei Ruggieri, active in Fontainbleau between 1557 and 1588. The panel like the *Birth of Cupid* by the same master in the Metropolitan Museum of Art (Béguin, pl. 75), is probably a fragment of a large composition.

Lent by Mr. Benjamin Rowland, Jr.

31.

TWO DRAWINGS FOR *ORLANDO FURIOSO*

JEAN-HONORÉ FRAGONARD (French), 1732-1806.
Chalk, brush, and bistre wash; 15 x 9½″.

In the 1780s, Fragonard illustrated a good part of Ludovico Ariosto's early 16th-century epic *Orlando Furioso* with 137 drawings. They are works of brilliance seldom equaled in the Rococo era.

The first example (a) illustrates Canto X, ottavo 65, where Melissa, assisted by Ruggiero and Astolfo, speaks with the fairy Logistilla. Fragonard has captured the sense of magic and mystery surrounding these supernatural haunts. Washes of varying intensities — from the lighter regions below to the darker areas in the vaulting above — convey a sense of the billowing air and dense atmosphere found in "questi bei giardini" (ottavo 62). Specific details become mere dots as the artist seeks not to portray a realistic scene but a moment of fantasy and adventure.

The second drawing (b) illustrates Canto XVI, ottavo 32. Rinaldo reminds his knights of their debt to God, who has gathered them all together, and promises that worldly glory will soon come to them. Here the artist has depicted a scene that is light and open in comparison with the dramatic *chiaroscuro* of the above example. Rinaldo's exhortation to his troops, the banners and plumage flying in the wind, and the angel guiding the men on their way — all drawn with an agitated, quickly moving line — convey an excitement and a passion that faithfully represent the mood and wording of the epic poem itself.

BIBLIOGRAPHY: E. Mongan, P. Hofer, and J. Seznec, *Fragonard Drawings for Ariosto*, 1945, pp. 69, 77, pls. 62, 120.

Lent by Mr. Arthur A. Houghton, Jr.

32.

ARAB HORSEMAN ON PATROL

EUGÈNE DELACROIX (French), 1798-1836.
Oil on canvas; 22 x 18⅛″.

EXHIBITIONS: *Exposition des Oeuvres d'Eugène Delacroix*, Société National des Beaux-Arts, Paris, 1864, No. 94; *Loan Exhibition of Paintings, Water Colors, Drawings, and Prints by Eugène Delacroix*, Art Institute of Chicago, March 20-April 20, 1930, No. 36; *An Exhibition of the Alexander M. Byers Collection of Paintings*, Carnegie Institute, Pittsburgh, Jan. 8-March 15, 1932, No. 17 (called *The Signal*); *The Romantic Revolt*, Springfield Museum of Fine Arts, Springfield, Mass., Feb. 7-March 5, 1939, No. 17; *Eugène Delacroix*, Wildenstein Gallery, New York,

Oct. 18-Nov. 18, 1944, No. 33; *Loan Exhibition of Masterpieces by Delacroix and Renoir*, Rosenberg Gallery, New York, Feb. 16-March 13, 1948, No. 7.

In 1832 Delacroix journeyed to Morocco. His experiences there inspired those paintings of the 1840s and 1850s in which exotic and dramatic themes of Arabs and animals are prevalent. The theme of this painting (signed and dated 1851) provided an excellent vehicle through which Delacroix could express vigorous movement — as in the horse's turned head and the Arab's signaling arm — and exploit the emotional impact of sensuous, heated colors — as in the horseman's billowing red cloak.

BIBLIOGRAPHY: General reference: R. Huyghe, *Delacroix*, 1963 (trans. from French by J. Griffin).

Anonymous Loan

33.

LEAVING THE THEATER

HONORÉ DAUMIER (French), 1808-1879.
Oil on canvas; 13¼ x 16½".

EXHIBITIONS: *Exposition Daumier*, Ecole des Beaux-Arts, Paris, May 1901, No. 95; *Frankfurter Kunstschatze*, Frankfurter Kunstverein, Frankfurt, July 20-Sept. 20, 1913, No. 18; *Austellung Honoré Daumier*, Galerie Matthiesen, Berlin, Feb. 21-March 21, 1926, No. 17; *The French Revolution*, Wildenstein Gallery, New York, Dec. 1943, No. 419; The Rhode Island School of Design, Providence, 1945.

By 1848 Daumier was already famous for his political caricatures (for which he had been jailed briefly in 1832). As a painter, however, he had no financial success, and he died in poverty. The daily life of lower-class Parisians and the plight of mankind are the themes he most frequently used in his paintings. Daumier absorbed influences from Rubens, Rembrandt, and the contemporary Barbizon painters and formulated a style of broad sweeping brushstrokes with which he portrayed the outstanding features of individual faces in the context of an anonymous crowd. In its poignant mood and "lonely crowd" theme, this work may be compared with the artist's well-known *Third-Class Carriage* in the Metropolitan Museum of Art.

BIBLIOGRAPHY: R. Escholier, *Daumier*, 1923, p. 100; E. Fuchs, *Der Maler Daumier*, 1930, pl. 40; J. Lassaigne, *Daumier*, pl. 130.

Lent by Mr. Charles W. Engelhard

34.

HUNTERS IN THE SNOW

GUSTAVE COURBET (French), 1819-1877.
Oil on canvas; 19¼ x 25½".

EXHIBITIONS: *Exposition Courbet*, Bernheim-Jeune, Paris, Dec. 21, 1917-Jan. 5, 1918, No. 11.

In the 1860s the emphasis in Courbet's painting changed from depictions of social problems in contemporary life to scenes of a more personal nature — nudes, landscapes, and still life. During 1858-59 Courbet had been in Frankfurt on a hunting vacation; this experience engendered the hunting scenes of the next decade, many reminiscent of Breughel.

This painting, signed and dated "66 Gustave Courbet", is an investigation into the pictorial possibilities of snow. The vastness of the space is due in part to the high horizon against which figures and tree are silhouetted, and in part to the broad expanse of the white snow itself.

BIBLIOGRAPHY: J. Meier-Graefe, *Courbet*, 1921; C. Leger, *Courbet*, 1929; H. Naef, *Courbet*, 1947; M. Zahar, *Gustave Courbet*, 1952.

Lent by Mr. Charles W. Engelhard

35.

THE NURSE

MARY CASSATT (American), 1844-1926.
Oil on canvas; 28⅞ x 36¼".

EXHIBITIONS: *Nineteenth-Century French Painters*, M. Knoedler and Co., London, 1923, No. 4; Minneapolis Institute of Arts, April-May 1930, No. 4; *Exhibition of 19-Century and Contemporary Watercolors*, Art Museum of the New Britain Institute, May-June 1943, No. 53.

In 1877 Degas invited Mary Cassatt, daughter of a wealthy Pittsburgh banker, to become a member of the French Impressionist group. Both the general characteristics of Impressionism and Degas' particular influence on Cassatt are apparent in this painting. Like the Impressionists, she painted casual, undramatic moments culled from daily life. Among her favorite subjects were mother and child scenes. In this painting we see a variation of this theme: a nurse and two children sit drenched in sunlight at the end of a garden path. The off-center focus of the composition is typical of Cassatt and was undoubtedly influenced by both Degas and Japanese prints.

BIBLIOGRAPHY: General reference: *The Paintings of Mary Cassatt,*
(catalogue of exhibition at M. Knoedler and Co., New York), 1966.

Lent by Mr. A. Varick Stout

36.

THE FARMHOUSE AT LE POULDU

PAUL SERUSIER (French), 1863-1927.
Oil on canvas; 28½ x 23¾".

The Farmhouse at Le Pouldu (signed and dated 1890) is a painting in which no story is told. It is not the peasant's relationship to farmhouse or landscape which is crucial to our enjoyment, but rather such formal qualities as the sensuous and decorative melting together of liquid shapes in the foreground, or the jolting sensations of cold blues and greens against warm orange-golds and purples. This emphasis on the expressive potential of colors and shapes is something the artist learned from Gauguin.

BIBLIOGRAPHY: J. Rewald, *Post Impressionism: from Van Gogh to Gauguin*, 1956, p. 293.

Lent by Mr. Alexander M. Laughlin

37.

CLASSICAL LANDSCAPE

RICHARD WILSON, R. A. (English), 1714-1782.
Black and white chalk on buff paper; 12 x 18⅜".

Richard Wilson is a particularly important figure in the history of English landscape painting. From 1751/2 to 1757/8 he worked in Rome. There under the influence of the French seascape and landscape painter Claude Joseph Vernet, Wilson himself became a landscapist; formerly, he had been primarily a portraitist. This drawing, probably executed during his Roman sojourn, reveals Wilson's interest in such 17th-century French landscape painters as Claude Lorrain and Gaspard Dughet, both of whom also worked in Rome. In particular, the cliff in the middleground with the buildings atop is a favorite Dughet compositional motif. Wilson grafted a taste for classical composition and atmospheric poetry onto the native English tradition of topographical exactitude, and laid the pictorial groundwork for later English artists like Constable and Turner.

BIBLIOGRAPHY: W. G. Constable, *Richard Wilson*, 1953.

Lent by Professor and Mrs. E. Dudley H. Johnson

38.
NEAR DEDHAM
JOHN CONSTABLE (English), 1776-1837.
Oil on panel; 7½ x 16¼".

In his total commitment to an honest portrayal of deep feeling for nature and rural life, John Constable limited himself to the depiction of only a few locations which he knew and loved: Brighton, Hampstead, Salisbury, and Dedham in his native Suffolk. Constable continually studied and represented the complex effects of changing weather, nature, and sky conditions on the rural countryside. Through his use of short brushstrokes of brightly colored paint, he exhibited within the context of these empirical investigations his love for the English countryside and his delight in all real things.

BIBLIOGRAPHY: G. Reynolds, *Constable the Natural Painter*, 1965;
J. Baskett, *Constable Oil Sketches*, 1966.   *Lent by Mr. and Mrs. James Biddle*

39.
FOUR STUDIES OF AENEAS FLEEING THE BURNING TROY
WILLIAM ETTY (English), 1787-1849.
Pencil; 13⅛ x 20¼".

EXHIBITIONS: *Exhibition of Old Master Drawings at the H. Shickman Gallery*, New York, October 1965, No. 64.

Through his use of short brushtrokes of brightly colored paint, he exhibited within the context of nude or semi-nude human forms, minimizing literary or psychological overtones in his works. In doing this, he was continuing and combining the traditions of Rubens and the Venetians and the system of academic copying from the live model. Etty attended the life classes at the Royal Academy in London, and produced many purely formal academic studies of the nude, which illustrate his technical proficiency as well as his desire to impart a sensual quality to the human figure. When combined, these separate studies would form a large-scale subject painting.

BIBLIOGRAPHY: A. Gilchrist, *The Life of William Etty, R. A.*, 1955;
D. Farr, *William Etty*, 1958.   *Lent by Mr. Frederick B. Adams*

INTRODUCTION:

English Nineteenth-Century Watercolors

Early nineteenth-century England saw many of its artists painting watercolor landscapes. Indeed, the use of the watercolor medium was found to be consonant with the desire to render the quickly changing weather and atmospheric conditions of haziness, cloudiness, and dampness peculiar to the English countryside. The thin translucent washes were better than thicker paints for capturing ephemeral conditions; they aided in diverting attention from interest in topographical rendering or creating a landscape setting for a subject painting to a new breadth of unified atmospheric impressions where mood or a close empirical study of nature reigned.

The combined influences of Thomas Girtin, John Cotman, and William Turner changed the status of the watercolor from a sketch or preparatory drawing to a finished work of art. Also important was the new position that the landscape occupied in English taste—that of a picturesque or idyllic haven for fugitives from the smoke and squalor of the cities of the industrial revolution.

In 1804 the Old Water Colour Society was formed. Its first exhibitions were so successful that in 1810, the Royal Academy repealed its laws which had excluded painters of watercolors from membership. Later a trend developed toward the obliteration of distinctions inherent within the two techniques, for works in both media were exhibited side by side in the same heavy gilt frames. Watercolorists sought to rival the rich chromatic effects attained in the heavier oil medium, and it is interesting to note that in their later years Cotman and Cox began to paint in both oil and watercolor. Watercolor, however, was used primarily to capture the transience of English climatic conditions and their effects upon nature.

C. Nachmani

40.
THE LAKE OF NEMI
JOHN ROBERT COZENS (English), 1752-1797.
Watercolor; 14½ x 21".

John Robert Cozens was the son and pupil of Alexander Cozens. After his trip to Italy in 1776 as a draftsman for Richard Payne Knight, an eminent authority on Picturesque aesthetic theory and a collector of antique sculpture, Cozens came under the influence of Claude Lorrain. This can be seen in compositions such as *The Lake of Nemi* (signed and dated 1789), where parallel layers recede with an even rhythm and create a measured space into depth. The French landscapist's influence is also evident in Cozens' use of silhouetted objects and people. Cozens became famous for his ability to establish the qualities and moods of a particular landscape by the use of elegant rhythms within the context of a limited range of controlled colors. In his desire to capture the specific atmosphere and mood of a landscape, he is a precursor of Constable and Turner.

BIBLIOGRAPHY: C. F. Bell and T. Girtin, "The Drawings and Sketches of John Robert Cozens," *Walpole Society: Annual Volume*, XXIII, 1934-35, No. 143; A. P. Oppé, *Alexander and John Robert Cozens*, 1952.

Lent by Mr. and Mrs. James Biddle

41.
THE DEATH OF ST. JOSEPH
WILLIAM BLAKE (English), 1757-1827.
Watercolor; 25 x 25".

For William Blake, both poetry and visual illustration were integral parts in the materialization of his visions. These were made tangible through the use of a precise but mannered line which circumscribed flattened bodies in a flattened space. *The Death of St. Joseph* can be dated c.1803, for it was one of a series of Biblical illustrations executed in watercolor for Thomas Butts during the years 1800-5. During this interim, Blake's previously pessimistic conceptions of an evil universe which offered little hope for man's salvation were transformed into a belief that man, through the proper use of his senses, could liberate himself. In the Biblical illustrations, therefore, there is the consequent emphasis on the spiritual triumph of good over evil. In this work, the elongated religious figures are illuminated by a supernatural radiance; and the compositional reduction of elements and repetition of forms contribute to the pervasive ethereal quality of the painting.

BIBLIOGRAPHY: Sir G. Keynes, *William Blake's Illustrations to the Bible*, 1957; Sir A. Blunt, *The Art of William Blake*, 1959 (contains full bibliography).   *Lent by Mr. and Mrs. James Biddle*

42.
MAINZ AND KASTELL
JOSEPH MALLORD WILLIAM TURNER (English), 1775-1851.
Watercolor; 8⁵⁄₁₆ x 14¾".

EXHIBITIONS: *Old Masters*, Royal Academy, London, 1889, No. 23; Lawrie Galleries, London, 1902, No. 21; *Turner, Cox and de Wint*, Agnew's, London, 1924, No. 25; *British Art*, Royal Academy, 1934, No. 904; *Centenary Loan Exhibition of Turner's Watercolours*, Agnew's, 1951, No. 57.

This painting, one of fifty-one watercolor views of the Rhine, was executed by Turner after a small drawing in one of three sketchbooks he filled during his tour of the Rhine in 1817. Already at this date there appears a unity of light, sky, and water in an enveloping atmosphere, which conveys a sense of spatial depth. Turner applied watercolors in various ways. He used heavy or light, dry or wet washes, body paint, or dry paint in order to create different textures on his paper.

BIBLIOGRAPHY: A. J. Finberg, *The Life of J. M. W. Turner, R. A.*, 1939 (2nd edition, revised by H. Finberg, 1961); M. Butlin, *Turner Watercolours*, 1962; J. Lindsay, *J. M. W. Turner: A Critical Biography*, 1966.   *Lent by Mr. and Mrs. James Biddle*

43.
LANDSCAPE WITH A RUINED ABBEY
JOHN SELL COTMAN (English), 1782-1842.
Watercolor; 6½ x 9¾".

In 1806 John Sell Cotman joined the Norwich Society of Artists. One of the leading watercolorists of the Norwich School, he became an Associate of the Old Water Colour Society in 1825.

Cotman's approach to nature differed from that of his contemporary watercolorists. He desired to supplant their realistic orientation with his own aesthetic one, in which natural forms were transformed into surface patterns. In this painting, the hilly expanses of land under rolling skies are achieved by means of patterns composed of meandering outlines and large, flat, delicately colored washes.

BIBLIOGRAPHY: A. P. Oppé, *The Water-Colour Drawings of John Sell Cotman*, 1923; S. Kitson, *The Life of John Sell Cotman*, 1937; V. Rienaecker, *John Sell Cotman*, 1953.
Lent by Professor and Mrs. E. Dudley H. Johnson

44.
FERNS, GRASS, AND FLOWERS
WILLIAM HENRY HUNT (English), 1790-1864.
Gouache; 20 x 17".

When William Henry Hunt became a member of the Old Water Colour Society in England in 1826, he changed his painting medium from oil to watercolor and his subject matter from topographical landscapes to a more poetic view of nature. He limited his output to small drawings and paintings of still life elements: birds' nests, flowers, and foliage. These were portrayed realistically with sharply defined brushstrokes in opaque body color (gouache). This elaborate attention to minute detail interested the members of the Pre-Raphaelite Brotherhood and their defender, John

Ruskin. The trend toward acute realism of detail in landscape soon became an identifying characteristic of Pre-Raphaelite painting.

BIBLIOGRAPHY: *The Works of John Ruskin*, ed. by E. T. Cook and Alexander Wedderburn
(Library Edition), XIV, pp. 373-84, 440-48; F. G. Stephens, "William Henry Hunt,
The Old Water Colour Society's Club, XII (1935) pp. 17-50.   *Lent by Mr. and Mrs. James Biddle*

45.
SHIPPING OFF SHORE WITH APPROACHING STORM
WLLIAM PURSER (English), 1805-1834.
Watercolor; 12 x 14½".

In this watercolor seascape, the technical properties of the medium are used to best advantage to capture the transience of windswept sea, storm-tossed clouds, and windblown sails. The transparency of the paint and the quickness of its application allowed Purser to record the ephemeral moment as the sky and sea interact to produce conditions unsafe for man. Indeed, the precarious position of the men in the storm — who are represented by small dabs of paint — is emphasized by the contrasting background, a "tasteful," picturesque view of a nearby castle on a rugged mountain cliff.

Lent by Mr. and Mrs. James Biddle

46.
A FALCONER
SIR EDWIN HENRY LANDSEER, R. A. (English), 1802-1873.
Watercolor and pencil; 10 x 7".

EXHIBITIONS: *Sir Edwin Landseer, R. A.*, Royal Academy, London, 1961.

Sir Edwin Landseer gained wide acclaim and popularity during the Victorian period. He was, perhaps, most favored for sentimental paintings in which animals, acting out the vicissitudes of everyday dramas and fashionable anecdotes, and expressing human emotions, took on the attributes of men. *A Falconer*, executed in 1837, is quite different. It shows Landseer's interest (characteristic of the age) in the close empirical study of the natural world.

Lent by Professor and Mrs. E. Dudley H. Johnson

47.
STUDY OF TREES
EDWARD LEAR (English), 1812-1888.
Charcoal and wash; 24 x 18".

EXHIBITIONS: *Edward Lear: 1812-1888*, Aldeburg Festival (Arts Council), 1958.

In the third decade of the 19th century Lear specialized in the drawing of birds, especially parrots. He was forced to give it up because of eyestrain, and therefore, at the time of his trip to Rome in 1837, he switched to landscape painting. The influence of his Italian visit can be seen in the *Study of Trees*, signed and dated 1839. The drawing exhibits the beginning of Lear's tendency toward a calligraphic, linear form of expression. This was later reinforced by the influence of Holman Hunt's bright colors and precise realistic detail, when in 1852 Lear became Hunt's student.

BIBLIOGRAPHY: A. Davidson, *Edward Lear: Landscape Painter and Nonsense Poet*, 1938.

Lent by Mr. and Mrs. James Biddle

48.

THE SPLÜGEN PASS
JOSEPH MALLORD WILLIAM TURNER (English), 1775-1851.
Watercolor; 11½ x 17¾″.

EXHIBITIONS:*Ruskin's Collection of Turner Water Colours*, Fine Art Society, 1878; *Old Masters*, Royal Academy, 1886, No. 22; *Turner Exhibition*, Guildhall, 1899, No. 159; *Ruskin's Collection of Turner Water Colours*, Fine Art Society, 1900, No. 50; *Old Masters*, Royal Academy, 1901, No. 119 (lent by Mrs. Severn); *Turner Water Colours*, Agnew's, 1913, No. 22; *Ruskin and His Circle*, Arts Council, 1964, No. 101; *Fine Paintings from Gloucestershire Houses*, 21st Cheltenham Festival, July 1965, No. 46.

The Splügen Pass (1842), based on drawings Turner made during his trip to Switzerland in 1841, is one of four finished watercolor views of Swiss scenes. The use of light and atmosphere as elemental forces that pervade the universe and cause solid matter to dissolve within the painting is combined with a sketchy execution. In this and his other later landscapes, Turner was able to blend a sense of mystical pantheism with a close empirical study of nature.

BIBLIOGRAPHY: A. J. Finberg, *The Life of J. M. W. Turner, R. A.*, 1939 (2nd edition revised by H. Finberg, 1961); M. Butlin, *Turner Watercolours*, 1962; J. Lindsay, *J. M. W. Turner: A Critical Biography*, 1966.
Lent by Mr. and Mrs. James Biddle

49.

HAYMAKING IN WALES
DAVID COX (English), 1783-1859.
Watercolor; 10 x 13¾″.

In the windswept fields of the Welsh countryside filled with harvesters, workers, and other rural folk, David Cox found his earliest inspirations for landscape paintings. He possessed great love for nature and portrayed it with either dramatic intensity or anecdotal charm. After 1844, Cox painted primarily in Bettws-y-Coed, Wales, because of the grandeur of its scenery and its "truly rural state of nature." *Haymaking in Wales* is signed and dated 1850. About this time, Cox's compositions were looser and his style was more blotty, vague, and rough than in his earlier works. He said of his last paintings, "... these are the works of the mind, which I consider very far before portraits of places."

BIBLIOGRAPHY: F. G. Roe, *Cox the Master*, 1946; T. Cox, *David Cox*, 1947.
Lent by Professor and Mrs. E. Dudley H. Johnson

50.

THE WATERFALL AT PISTIL MAWDDACH, NEAR DOLGELLY, N. WALES
SAMUEL PALMER (English), 1805-1881.
Watercolor; 18½ x 14⅝″.

According to Geoffrey Grigson, this watercolor was probably executed during Palmer's first visit to Wales in 1835. At this time Palmer was evolving a style far removed from the mannered linearism of his Shoreham period with its dependency on both Dutch landscapes and the artist William Blake. The earlier Shoreham style was supplanted by subdued idealism and concern for panoramic breadth. The new style was a more poetic personal landscape, based partly on the influence of Claude Lorrain. In this watercolor, signed and inscribed by the painter, Palmer has caught the freshness and spontaneity of the waterfall and surrounding scenery.

BIBLIOGRAPHY: G. Grigson, *Samuel Palmer, The Visionary Years*, 1947; M. Butlin, *Samuel Palmer's Sketch-Book*, 1824, 1962.
Lent by Mr. and Mrs. James Biddle

American Art

AMERICAN ART

Eighteenth - Nineteenth Centuries

Introduction: American Nineteenth-Century Painting

With the opening of the nineteenth century, America entered her second decade of nationhood. Meeting the responsibilities and challenges of independence with optimism and eagerness, her people began to develop a national consciousness, priding themselves in their democratic experiment and in the magnitude and wealth of their continent. It is no surprise to find that this century of continental expansion, technological growth, and national maturation supported an ever-increasing number of American amateur and professional artists who attempted to forge an idiom uniquely expressive of America's national identity.

Their self-conscious struggle to establish a basis for American culture was buttressed by nineteenth-century Romanticism, which valued not only a love of country but also an emotional response to nature and the world. At the same time, the Romantic artists, sensing the impermanence of man and his civilizations, found inspiration in the Past. Yet where could Americans find their country's past and heritage? What institutions, customs, literary or artistic expressions could provide a sense of national history in a new land?

No one felt more insecure in this dilemma than the nation's budding artists and writers. Many of them felt the lack of the traditional artistic sources — time-honored customs, varied social classes, and the ruins of centuries. No continuity of artistic tradition had ever been established in America, nor had her citizens ever had the time or will to focus attention on the training and support of the arts. All through the century artists and writers bemoaned the absence of national art academies, publishing houses, museums, a public taste for high culture, and, above all, an individual American expression independent of European modes.

Our most sensitive artists, however, answered Emerson's basic challenge to his countrymen: to discover and to rely on their own means of shaping the American experience into appropriate artistic forms. Most conspicuously, artists began to uncover a Past and a Present in the American scene. Herman Melville wove the intricacies of the New England whaling industry into a novel of international stature while Henry David Thoreau found his worldly travels and primitive beauties in a small pond outside of Concord, Massachusetts. The almost exclusive concentration of the seventeenth- and eighteenth-century painters on portraiture suddenly gave way to a full, experimental range of native subject matter. A growing landscape school discovered indigenous beauty and drama in America's undeveloped wilderness. Genre painters such as George Caleb Bingham and Eastman Johnson began to record the peculiar mannerisms and local color of the country's regions and social classes. Other artists took an intense interest in pictorially preserving the unique dress and character of the vanishing American Indian or the plumage and variety of America's birds.

While this discovery of America produced a multitude of expressions, American artists still depended on European models for many aspects of technique and composition. No longer attached to the colonial tradition of study and apprenticeship in England, many of them roamed the continent, attending the art schools in France, Germany, and Italy. American painters participated, if only peripherally, in the European international movement from Romanticism to Realism and Impressionism. This general pattern can be easily discerned in the successive landscapes of Cole (No. 55), Church (No. 60), Heade (Nos. 63, 64), and Homer (Nos. 70, 71).

For the new nation, however, the age is characterized by the growing independence and maturation of all her arts, a striving toward the artistic establishment of a usable past, an honorable present, and a promise for the future.

W. Corn

51.
WINE-TASTER
HENRICUS BOELEN (American), 1697-1755.
Silver, weight 3.10 ounces; diameter 4½".

This bowl, like the Bancker tankard (No. 52), reflects the simple taste of the colonial American. In spite of their simplicity, however, such objects were quite valuable and scarce. They showed that the owner could afford the many silver pieces that needed to be melted down to make such a vessel.

The plain shape of the bowl provides an interesting foil for the two twisted wire handles which, by contrast, seem somewhat "baroque" and ornate. In addition, the artist uses the beautifully shaped voids created by the handles to stress the solidity and substance of the small bowl. Henricus Boelen, the creator of this early American masterpiece, was the master of Adrian Bancker, the silversmith of the following tankard.

BIBLIOGRAPHY: Unpublished. General reference: C. L. Avery, *Early American Silver*, 1930.
Lent by Mr. Gardner D. Stout

52.

TANKARD

ADRIAN BANCKER (American), 1703-1772.
Silver, weight 8.2 ounces; height 4⅛″.

EXHIBITIONS: *Silver by New York Makers*, Museum of the City of New York, 1937-38, No. 15.

The early New York tankard was a descendant of the English tankard of the second half of the 17th century. The severe simplicity of this object, however, may very well reflect Dutch taste which persisted in the New York region even after New Amsterdam changed its allegiance in 1664. New York silver, in fact, brought together the silver traditions of both Holland and England.

The New York tankard is generally large, with a slight tapering in the shape and moldings at the base. A silver coin chosen for its decorative qualities was often inserted into the flat-topped cover. The coin in this tankard is inscribed with a Dutch poem dated 1678; the poem commemorates a peace concluded earlier that year at Nymwegen between the Dutch and the French. The extreme simplicity of the tankard's outline and its very plain surface provide a striking contrast to the more ornate Elizabethan tankards exhibited in this show (No. 18).

BIBLIOGRAPHY: Unpublished. General reference: C. L. Avery, *Early American Silver*, 1930.

Lent by Mr. Gardner D. Stout

53.

VIEWS OF THE BATTLES OF LEXINGTON AND CONCORD

AMOS DOOLITTLE (American), 1754-1832.
Colored engravings; 7½ x 13″.

EXHIBITIONS: *American Art from American Collections*, Metropolitan Museum of Art. 1963. Nos. 209-212.

Much of colonial American art was in the form of portraits and prints; both were often inspired by English or Continental examples. Engravings were executed in America under the impetus of an historical event rather than for purely aesthetic purposes, and they illustrate a provincialism and naiveté in the handling of figures and perspective. Amos Doolittle, an engraver and silversmith working in Connecticut, executed these prints after the sketches of the American portraitist, Ralph Earl (1751-1801), who had drawn them shortly after the events themselves occurred. Eight complete sets of the prints and a few single sheets exist. These prints therefore constitute a rare artistic commemoration of an historical occasion, as well as an early attempt at the creation of artistic expression in America.

BIBLIOGRAPHY: I. N. Phelps Stokes and D. C. Haskell, *American Historical Prints*, 1932.

Lent by Mr. Harry W. Havemeyer

54.

RED JACKET

JOHN NEAGLE (American), 1796-1865.
Oil on canvas; 26 x 21½″.

In this portrait, John Neagle merges two traditions common in American painting in the first half of the 19th century: concern for the accurate recording in portrait form of the physical characteristics of the individual and interest in illustrating the landscape and inhabitants — especially the Indian — of the American West. Neagle was the principal portrait painter in Philadelphia before the Civil War and practiced in the traditions of both Gilbert Stuart and Thomas Sully. This portrait of Sagoyewatha, a Seneca chief, was painted in 1824 on commision for William D. Lewis. It is an acute character study of the sitter mingled with genre interest in the costume and paraphernalia of the Indian chief.

Lent by Mr. Benjamin R. Neilson

55.

MILL DAM ON THE CATSKILL CREEK

THOMAS COLE (American), 1801-1848.
Oil on canvas; 22¼ x 30¼".

EXHIBITIONS: *Cole Memorial Show*, The American Art Union, 1848, No. 20.

Born in England, Cole came to America in his late teens, accomplished as an apprentice wood engraver but determined to become a painter. A short but successful career was ahead of him. One of the first American artists to make a living from the painting of landscapes, Cole was the acknowledged leader of the Hudson River School artists in his pioneering appreciation and depiction of the American landscape. In 1841, the same year that Cole painted this romantic upper New York scene, he delivered a Lyceum lecture on the beauties and splendors of the American land: "There are those who, through ignorance or prejudice, strive to maintain that American scenery possesses little that is interesting or truly beautiful; . . . But from whom do these opinions come? From those who have read of Grecian mountains and Italian skies, and never troubled themselves to look at their own?" Cole's landscape, with its radiant backlight suggesting vast distance and throwing the foreground into darkened relief, offers a view of classic order and serenity. The lessons offered by the 17th-century classical landscapists such as Claude Lorrain and Poussin have been masterfully imposed onto nature's irregular vistas.

BIBLIOGRAPHY: L. L. Noble, *The Life and Works of Thomas Cole*, 1853 (reprinted 1964).   *Lent by Mr. Henry M. Fuller*

56.

PORTRAIT OF MONCURE ROBINSON

THOMAS SULLY (American), 1783-1872.
Oil on canvas; 20¼ x 17".

Portrait painting remained the staple of American art throughout the first half of the 19th century; indeed, Thomas Sully was known to have executed almost two thousand portraits as well as five hundred subject paintings and landscapes. It was his fluent brushwork that gained him his reputation and helped establish the stately elegance, gentility, and Romantic character of his works. Many of his portraits show the subject silhouetted against a vaporous background, the personality reflecting melancholy or inward thoughts, and the posture and head betraying movement. These are very close to the English aristocratic portraits of Lawrence in their psychology, color, and brushwork. Sully executed a number of portraits of the Robinson family. This portrait of Moncure Robinson (1802-1891), an eminent civil engineer, was done in 1849.

BIBLIOGRAPHY: C. H. Hart, *A Register of Portraits Painted by Thomas Sully, 1801-1871*,
1909; E. Biddle and M. Fielding, *The Life and Work of Thomas Sully, 1783-1872*, 1921.

Lent by Mr. Alexander O. Vietor

57.

STAGE ROCKS AND WESTERN SHORE OF GLOUCESTER OUTER HARBOR

FITZ HUGH LANE (American), 1804-1865.
Oil on canvas; 23 x 38".

EXHIBITIONS: *Fitz Hugh Lane, The First Major Exhibition*, DeCordova Museum, Lincoln, Mass. and Colby College Art Museum, Waterville, Maine, 1966, No. 26.

Fitz Hugh Lane, a native of the coastal fishing town of Gloucester, Massachusetts, was a passionate admirer of the marine activity enlivening its shores and harbors. Already accomplished as a lithographer, he devoted the last fifteen years of his life almost exclusively to the painting of harbor views and seascapes of the eastern seaboard. Several preparatory drawings and a smaller oil version of this subject exist. This panoramic view of Gloucester Harbor, painted c.1852, is characteristic of Lane's subtle integration of topographically realistic detail with the diffused effects of light and atmosphere; these qualities link him to the American luminists of the 1850s and 1860s. The early morning quiet and magical stillness are intensified by the use of crisp, unbroken outlines which sharply silhouette the boats and hills against the sky and water. The compositional emphasis on the horizontal repetition of waves and landscape planes heightens the sense of supernatural calm.

BIBLIOGRAPHY: J. Wilmerding, *Fitz Hugh Lane, American Marine Painter*, 1964, p. 62; _____, "A Selection of Marine Paintings by Fitz Hugh Lane," *The American Neptune Pictorial Supplement*, VII (1965) pl. XVII; _____, "Fitz Hugh Lane, Painter of Gloucester," *Journey Through New England*, 3 (1966) pp. 72-74; _____, "Interpretation of Place: Views of Gloucester, Mass. by American Artists," *Essex Institute Historical Collections*, CIII, No. 1 (1967) pp. 53-65.   *Lent by Mr. John C. Wilmerding, Jr.*

58.

MISSISSIPPI FLATBOATMAN

GEORGE CALEB BINGHAM (American), 1811-1879.
Oil on canvas; 24 x 17½".

EXHIBITIONS: Philadelphia Art Union, 1851, No. 51.

In 1851, the Philadelphia Art Union laconically described this frontier genre piece (which was listed for sale at $60) as "an old man smoking his morning pipe at the Riverside." The river is the Mississippi and the scene as depicted by Bingham overflows with local Missouri color: the boatman's weathered, overgrown features and intense gaze, the candy-striped, open-necked blouse and peaked cap which identify his trade, the cargo barrels, the flatboat alongside, and the early morning river mist present a sober spectacle of regional manners. Bingham's paintings, however, are always more than picturesque illustrations of frontier life. He created beauty and grandeur out of the commonplace scenes of his home state. The artist's sure sense of construction and unequivocal lighting lock the Mississippi boatman into his space, presenting him both at home and as master of the scene, an austere backwoodsman Zeus on a wooden throne.

Mississippi Flatboatman is signed "G. C. Bingham, 1850."

BIBLIOGRAPHY: J. F. McDermott, *George Caleb Bingham, River Portraitist*, 1959, p. 416, No. 58; E. M. Block, *George Caleb Bingham*, 1967, I, p. 106, II, No. 194; J. Wilmerding, "George Caleb Bingham: a new find," *Antiques* XCII, No. 4 (1967) pp. 556-57.   *Lent by Mr. John C. Wilmerding, Jr.*

59.

PARTRIDGES OF AMERICA*

JOHN GOULD (English), 1804-1881.
Atlas folio, with contemporary green morocco binding and tooling by Zaehnsdorf of London.

John Gould, an eminent English ornithologist and painter of birds, published 41 folios on birds, including *Birds of Europe, Birds of Australia,* and *Birds of Great Britain.* Gould wrote the text and executed the lithographs for *Partridges of America,* which he published in London in 1850. The 32 plates are all hand-colored, contrasting the richly colored plumage of the partridges with the delicate drawing and pale washes of the backgrounds. They exemplify the increased mid-19th-century interest in scientific observation and rendering, readily seen by comparison with the earlier illustrations of Audobon.

Lent by Mr. Gardner D. Stout

*Not illustrated.

60.

SUNRISE IN THE CORDILLERAS

FREDERICK EDWIN CHURCH (American), 1826-1900.
Oil on canvas; 28½ x 43".

Challenged by the mid-19th-century quest to understand the physical universe, Frederick Church, our most renowned artist-explorer, journeyed to the corners of the Western world. Traveling to South America, Labrador, Jamaica, Europe and the Near East, he patiently sketched in oils the changing light conditions, geological formations, plants and vegetation. This tropical panorama of the Andes is a composite view painted by Church in 1854 in his New York City studio from sketches made during his first South American sojourn the previous year. The spectator's viewpoint is placed high, forcing the eye to plunge into the open vista and move over every inch of the canvas in order to absorb fully the spectacle and its wealth of detail. Each plateau offers something of interest: a South American hilltown; a roaring mountain cascade; native travelers journeying along a narrow path; untold varieties of scientifically rendered plant and tree forms; and reigning above all, the majestic raw peaks of the Andes.

BIBLIOGRAPHY: D. C. Huntington, *The Landscapes of Frederick Edwin Church, Vision of an American Era,* 1966.

Lent by Mr. John C. Wilmerding, Jr.

61.

WOODDUCK, GREEN-WINGED TEAL, AND BUFFLEHEAD

ARTHUR FITZWILLIAM TAIT (born England; U.S.A. 1850), 1819-1905.
Oil on wood panel; 15⅞ x 12".

Arthur Tait was principally a painter of wild animals and sporting scenes. This painting, signed and dated 1863, is a somewhat atypical work by the artist. Like Winslow Homer (see Nos. 70, 71), he often sketched in the Adirondacks, but unlike that New Englander, Tait concentrated on rendering exactly the minute variations in texture and the different anatomical details of his subject matter. Here, he skillfully contrasts the limp bodies of the dead birds with the taut strings that hold them flush against the nearly abstract background.

Tait became the principal illustrator for the lithographers Currier and Ives, who reproduced his depictions of animals for a growing American art public.

Lent by Mr. and Mrs. Pieter W. Fosburgh, Cherry Plain

62.
WOMAN POLISHING GLASSES
EASTMAN JOHNSON (American), 1824-1906.
Oil on canvas; 21 x 17".

Eastman Johnson's genre paintings form a chronicle of American manners in the late 19th century. The tastes and mood of bygone times are reflected in this somber interior in which a Victorian lady, undoubtedly preparing to read the large family Bible beside her, gingerly polishes her eyeglasses. Certain features of the painting — the horizontal and vertical lines which compose this domestic scene, the dark paint tonalities, and the windowband of sunlight illuminating the table, handkerchief, and face of the woman — are strongly reminiscent of the mannerisms of the 17th-century Dutch genre painters. It is no surprise to learn that, after studying in Germany, Johnson spent $3\frac{1}{2}$ years painting in Holland (1851-55). *Woman Polishing Glasses* is signed and dated 1863. Such intimate middle-class scenes, warm with atmosphere and homely details, earned Johnson the distinctive title of the "American Rembrandt."

BIBLIOGRAPHY: General reference: J. I. H. Baur, *An American Genre Painter, Eastman Johnson*, 1940.

Lent by Mr. Henry M. Fuller

63.
TWILIGHT IN THE SALT MARSHES
MARTIN JOHNSON HEADE (American), 1819-1904.
Charcoal; 11 x 21".

Martin Johnson Heade's work follows in the wake of the Hudson River School's establishment of native landscape painting as a viable and American means of expression. Unlike many of his contemporaries, however, Heade's approach to landscape was descriptive and realistic, without the aggrandizing and literary sentiments of Church or Bierstadt (see Nos. 60, 67). His themes present the gentle and modest faces of nature. This small charcoal drawing, executed c.1863-65, reveals Heade's delicate sensibility to light as a means of unifying and patterning the landscape. The slow static rhythms marked out by the haystacks, poplars, and sailboats are echoed in the receding patches of light and shadow. It is this carefully observed and at the same time poetic notation of light as it strikes across the passive marshes that has established Heade as one of our leading landscape luminists of the mid-19th century. It is perhaps because of his interest in changing sky and light reflections that Heade was attracted to the low-horizoned, flat marshlands; he painted and sketched them not only in Rhode Island but also in Florida and South America.

BIBLIOGRAPHY: T. E. Stebbins, Jr., *et al.*, *Luminous Landscape: The American Study of Light 1806-1870* (catalogue of exhibition at the Fogg Art Museum), 1966, p. 28.

Lent by Mr. John C. Wilmerding, Jr.

64.

LAKE ATITLÁN, GUATEMALA

MARTIN JOHNSON HEADE (American), 1819-1904.
Oil on canvas; 18½ x 36½″.

Heade, like the painter Frederick Church, was an inveterate traveler, and on several occasions he explored South America as a roving painter-naturalist. From sketches made on one of these expeditions, Heade painted a series depicting fabulous hummingbirds in their natural habitat, which he hoped to use as illustrations for a book on South American hummingbirds. Other paintings from his travels record with simple modesty the local shores and waterways of the South American landscape. In *Lake Atitlán* (signed and dated "Heade, 67"), the luminous and open sky, dramatically pierced by the lone mountain peak, acts as a shimmering foil to the shadowy foreground of exotic palm trees and peasant activity.

Lent by Mr. John C. Wilmerding, Jr.

65.

STILL LIFE: RED CHERRIES

ROBERT S. DUNNING (American), 1829-1905.
Oil on canvas; 6½ x 9″.

Robert Dunning was born in Maine and later moved to Massachusetts where he established himself in the firm of "Grouard & Dunning, artists" as a painter of portraits, genre, and still life. It is less than usual to find a still life by a native of New England, where portraiture, landscape, and genre painting were the more common 19th-century forms of artistic expression. This intimate little work, which is signed and dated 1866, betrays Dunning's delight in capturing the enamel textures and reflections of the bright red cherries against the polished table and wooden basket. Although the arrangement of the fruit and basket is casual, the artist has heightened its simple beauty by giving us an oblique close-up view, uniting the round geometric forms in the brilliance of a common light source which rakes across the miniature canvas from the left.

Lent by Mr. Henry M. Fuller

66.

THE EAGLE'S NEST

JASPER CROPSEY (American), 1823-1900.
Oil on canvas; 8 x 12″.

Jasper Cropsey was a painter of the Hudson River School whose members were dedicated to the portrayal of the American countryside. Although they depicted broad, panoramic landscapes, their scenes are usually filled with the minutiae of plant and animal life. Cropsey, in *The Eagle's Nest* (1867), describes a quiet lake in the wilderness. The light-filled sky, against which are silhouetted the branches of a bare tree, and the reflected light in the water immediately bring to mind the 17th-century landscapist Claude Lorrain, to whom the artist and the entire Hudson River School were indebted.

Lent by Mr. and Mrs. Pieter W. Fosburgh, Cherry Plain

67.

CALIFORNIA REDWOODS

ALBERT BIERSTADT (American), 1830-1902.
Oil on canvas; 117 x 50".

A century ago, Bierstadt's meticulous paintings of the Rocky Mountains and American West fascinated an east coast public which itself would never venture beyond the boundaries of easy transportation. Aggrandizing the natural beauties of the American continent, Bierstadt revealed the hidden spectacle and wonders of the virginal hinterland. The California redwoods, so grand in scale and timeless in age, reduce man's stature to but an infinitesimal pinpoint in space. Bierstadt's sense of dramatic composition and filtered lighting is superb. The tall narrow canvas accentuates the dazzling proportions of the giant trees as they soar into space. The aged patriarch of the redwoods, with its remarkably expressive stunted arms, stretches upward, radiantly absorbing the sunlight and finding its echo in the luminous craggy treetop just visible in the distant background.

California Redwoods was probably painted in the early 1870s.

Lent by Mr. John C. Wilmerding, Jr.

68.

THE APPIAN WAY

JOHN LINTON CHAPMAN (American), 1839-1905.
Oil on canvas; 12¼ x 26¾".

Italy was the great artistic "Mecca" for the Romantic period. Flocking to Rome and the surrounding countryside, American painters, sculptors, literati, and tourists evoked a world of former times: the narrow medieval streets, the awesome space of St. Peter's, the peasants in colorful costumes, the ruins and picturesque shepherds. John Linton Chapman's father, John Gadsby Chapman, was a well-established resident artist of Rome; his son, born in Rome, followed professionally in his footsteps. Both father and son were etchers as well as painters, and this may have contributed to the younger Chapman's dryness of style and precision of detail.

In *The Appian Way* (signed and dated 1879), each fragment of statuary, paving stone, or inscription carved in the ancient rocks has been carefully recorded. The eye moves along these crumbling monuments of past grandeur to a distant view of Rome with its landmark, the dome of St. Peter's. The existence of a much larger version of this scene, painted by Chapman nine years earlier, suggests that this painting was commissioned as a copy for a patron who had admired the original work, or perhaps even painted by the artist for himself as a personal record of a memorable Roman vista.

BIBLIOGRAPHY: For 1870 version, see: *American Paintings for Public and Private Collections*, Hirschl & Adler Galleries, 1967, No. 74.

Lent by Mr. Henry M. Fuller

69.

THROUGH THE FIELDS

WINSLOW HOMER (American), 1836-1910.
Charcoal and Chinese white; 10 x 15".

EXHIBITIONS: *Loan Exhibition of Winslow Homer*, Wildenstein Gallery, New York, Feb. 19-Mar. 22, 1947, No. 97; *Homer-Johnson Exhibition*, Los Angeles County Museum, Summer 1949, No. 2; *Timeless Master Drawings*, Wildenstein Gallery, New York, Nov.-Dec., 1955, No. 145.

Through the Fields (1879) is a drawing typical of Winslow Homer's work of the 1870s. At this time he was interested in depicting genre scenes of young children — girls and boys picking berries, wading in the ocean, or relaxing on the beaches or vast green lawns of America. These works can be seen as a continuation of an American genre tradition that began early in the 19th century and was practiced by artists such as Eastman Johnson; Homer, however, was able to eliminate much of the sentimentality inherent in the earlier works, replacing it with a concern for line, pattern, color, and light. His desire for an overall design led to an emphasis on elegant rhythms of a line that both outlines figures and weaves its own continuous pattern.

BIBLIOGRAPHY: L. Goodrich, *Winslow Homer*, 1959; A. T. E. Gardner, *Winslow Homer*, 1961.

Lent by Mr. Charles W. Engelhard

70.

HUNTER AND DOG, ADIRONDACKS

WINSLOW HOMER (American), 1836-1910.
Watercolor; 13⅜ x 19½".

EXHIBITIONS: *Winslow Homer, A Retrospective Exhibition*, National Gallery of Art and Metropolitan Museum of Art, 1958-59, No. 132; *Winslow Homer in the Adirondacks*, Adirondack Museum, 1959, Blue Mountain Lake, New York, No. 11.

Homer frequently worked in watercolor during his vacations in the Adirondacks, painting, for the most part, intimate views of man living and working close to nature. Unlike many of his contemporaries, Homer never depicted large panoramic landscapes based on the traditional classical formulas of Claude Lorrain. The hunters that he shows do not kill for pleasure or sport but rather in order to eke out a living in the rugged northern forests.

The viewer is drawn directly into the woods with the hunter and his dog in this work of 1889. The footsteps of the approaching man and dog can almost be heard. Paradoxically, even though we are actually in the scene, the artist makes no attempt to define the foliage minutely leaf by leaf. Instead, he uses paint to depict patterns of light and dark so that we sense the sun filtering through the brush and the light flickering upon the leaves as the branches swing in the breeze.

BIBLIOGRAPHY: General reference: L. Goodrich, *Winslow Homer*, 1959; A. T. E. Gardner, *Winslow Homer*, 1961.

Lent by Mr. and Mrs. Pieter W. Fosburgh, Cherry Plain

71.

DEER DRINKING

WINSLOW HOMER (American), 1836-1910.
Watercolor; 13½ x 19½".

EXHIBITIONS: *Exposition d'Art Américain*, Association Franco-Americaine d'Expositions de Peinture et de Sculpture, Paris, May 18-June 25, 1923, No. 37; *An Exhibition of Watercolors by Winslow Homer*, Carnegie Institute, Sept. 9-Oct. 26, 1923, No. 38; *Winslow Homer Centenary Exhibition*, Whitney Museum of American Art, New York, Dec. 15, 1936-Jan. 15, 1937, No. 74; *Winslow Homer, A Retrospective Exhibition*, National Gallery of Art and Metropolitan Museum of Art, 1958-59, No. 144; *Winslow Homer in the Adirondacks*, Adirondack Museum, Blue Mountain Lake, New York, 1959, No. 48.

In this painting of a deer gracefully bending its neck toward the crystal lake, Homer has captured for all time the sensations of quiet and stillness which pervade the forest. This work, signed and dated "Homer 1892" and executed at the North Woods Club, New York, is another example of Homer's facility in the watercolor medium.

BIBLIOGRAPHY: L. Goodrich, *Winslow Homer*, 1959, pl. 58; A. T. E. Gardner, *Winslow Homer*, 1961.

Lent by Mr. Cortlandt P. Dixon

72.

STILL LIFE WITH POTTERY MUG, NEWSPAPER, PIPE, MATCHES, AND OYSTER CRACKER

JOHN FREDERICK PETO (American), 1854-1907.
Oil on wood frame; 3¾ x 6″.

EXHIBITIONS: *John F. Peto*, Brooklyn Institute of Arts and Sciences Museum, 1950.

The illusionistic still lifes of John Peto resemble very closely those of William Harnett who executed "smoking scenes" similar to the painting above; it was not until recently that the works of the two artists were separated. Peto's depiction of everyday objects in a *trompe l'oeil* space differs from Harnett's in several respects: in Peto's greater asymmetry of composition and contrast of light and dark, his more painterly application of pigment, shallower spacial depth, and less realistic detail. Peto also was more interested in surrounding his still-life objects with a soft outline and atmosphere than in the re-creation on his canvas of each detail, texture, and surface of an object from the real world.

BIBLIOGRAPHY: A. Frankenstein, "Harnett, True and False," *Art Bulletin*
(March 1949) pp. 38-59.   *Lent by Mr. Frank T. Howard*

73.

TWENTY-THREE PEARS

JOSEPH DECKER (American), 1853-1924.
Oil on canvas; 24 x 11″.

The desire to render in a super-realistic fashion objects from the real world was shared by Harnett, Peto, and Decker. However, whereas the first two painters concentrated on a horizontal arrangement of different objects in a *trompe l'oeil* space, Decker created a vertical composition in which one kind of object is seen from different angles and in various positions. While each piece of fruit is given its slight imperfection and placed seemingly at random, the composition is well planned in the juxtaposition of pointed leaf and rounded pear and of dark and light. This arrangement and the denial of space or atmosphere gives the painting a decorative aesthetic existence of its own beyond the actual realistic representation.

Lent by Mr. Stuart C. Welch, Jr.

Twentieth-Century Western Art

74.

POMONA WITH LOWERED ARMS

ARISTIDE MAILLOL (French), 1861-1944.

Bronze; height 65⅜".

Maillol confined his sculpture almost exclusively to the celebration of the female form. Reacting early against the heightened emotionalism and intense modeling of Rodin and his many followers, Maillol never allowed the surface textures and tensions of his work to dominate the forms themselves. His figures do not contort in violent movement or passion; rather they belong to the ancient tradition of seeking an ideal harmony and equilibrium of parts in a figure of classic grace and earthbound calm. As Maillol explained: "I seek architecture and volume. Sculpture is architecture, the balance of masses, a composition with taste."

Pomona, the Roman goddess of fruit, was one of the artist's favorite themes. While the leaves that garland her hair and the apples in her open hands are her specific attributes, the smooth rounded lines of her ample limbs and the graceful flow of one form into another epitomize her symbolic qualities — fertility, lushness, maturity, and abundance.

BIBLIOGRAPHY: W. George, *Aristide Maillol*, 1965, fig. 206.   *Lent by Mr. R. Sturgis Ingersoll*

75.

RAPE OF EUROPA

JACQUES LIPCHITZ (born Lithuania; American), born 1891.

Bronze; height 34".

The prodigious creativity of Lipchitz has spanned and enriched almost the entire 20th century. Making an important contribution to Cubist sculpture in the early decades of the century, Lipchitz' work then moved into the deep ancestral lineage of such monumental sculptors as Bernini and Rodin. Challenged by the heroic themes of ancient myths, Lipchitz has created a pantheon of figure pieces symbolizing the struggles, conflicts, and passions fundamental to human existence.

This version of the *Rape of Europa* was created during the years of the Second World War when Lipchitz, an exiled Jew, was acutely aware of the war's inhumanities. The heavy modeled forms textured by the touch and marking of the sculptor's tools, the brilliantly restless silhouette, the play of volumes against voids, and the sensitivity to the dramatic capture of flickering light on the surface are the personal hallmarks of his energetic and heroic style.

BIBLIOGRAPHY: A. M. Hammacher, *Jacques Lipchitz, His Sculpture*, 1961, No. 59.   *Lent by Mr. R. Sturgis Ingersoll*

76.

THE ENCOUNTER

ALEXANDER CALDER (American), born 1898.

Black sheet metal; 16¼ x 19".

EXHIBITIONS: *Alexander Calder*, Museum of Modern Art, New York, 1951;
Calder Exhibition Catalogue, Solomon R. Guggenheim Museum, New York.

Calder's stabiles, constructed of flat sheets of painted black metal, illustrate full repose in sculpture and cessation of the movement seen in his earlier mobiles. *The Encounter* (1956), instead of being composed of linear wire outlines which move physically through air, is made of heavier, solid sculptural bodies which sit solidly in space. But space flows through the mass of the sculpture and becomes a vital constituent of the composition.

BIBLIOGRAPHY: H. H. Arnason, *Calder*, 1966.   *Lent by Mr. Lee A. Ault*

77.

STANDING GIRL WITH HAND ON HEAD

GERHARD MARCKS (German), born 1889.

Bronze; height 31⅞".

EXHIBITIONS: *Gerhard Marcks*, Walker Art Center, Minneapolis, Minn., 1953; *Gerhard Marcks, Skulpturen, Handzeichnungen, Druckgraphik*, Nationalgalerie, Berlin, 1958.

The works of Gerhard Marcks belong to the Expressionist tradition in sculpture which had its inception in northern European countries in the last decade of the 19th and first years of the 20th centuries. The *Standing Girl* (dated 1960), which resembles the earlier works of the sculptor Wilhelm Lehmbruck and Georg Kolbe of standing nude figures, places an emphasis on the internalized, introspective emotions of the generalized human form. The latter then becomes the vehicle for symbolic and expressive attitudes. The introversion of the figure is seen in the elongation of proportions, the simplification and almost geometrizing of the smooth rounded forms, the emphasis on hands and head as expressive devices, and the sense of arrested movement in the figure as it turns inward away from its enviroment.

Lent by Mr. Paul M. Ingersoll

78.

LA COLUMNA

EDGAR NEGRET (Colombian), born 1920.

Iron; height 27".

Negret represented his native Colombia at the 1958 Venice Biennale. His sculptures are in the collections of many modern art museums, including those in Caracas, Bogotá, Santiago de Chile, and New York City. The artist lived for a time in New York, but in 1963 returned to his home in Colombia.

La Columna (1964), in its tantalizing interplay of solids and voids, follows in the Cubist-Constructivist tradition of space-defining forms. The changing surfaces of Negret's column captivate the eye as they uncoil in an upward spiral and lean weightlessly into space.

Lent by Mr. Lee A. Ault, III

79.

AU CAFÉ

PABLO PICASSO (Spanish), born 1881.
Pastel; 12 x 15¼".

Picasso's blue period paintings (1901-4) never tell us much about the shadowy people who inhabit them. While the setting and dress of *Au Café* (1902) suggest that this couple is impoverished, we have no other clues as to who they are, how they relate to one another, or what they are thinking; we are aware only of a general but pervasive mood of introspective melancholy. Picasso skillfully uses empathetic forms, colors, and enigmatic gestures to carry this oppressive sense of gloom and despair: the monochromatic use of blue, the compact forms of the figures shrinking into themselves, the ambiguous glances which do not make contact or communicate, the commanding shape of the ovoid table holding two isolated glasses, and the contrast between the dimly lit scene of the distant café dancer and the murky shadows enveloping the couple all contribute to a specific state of mind. It has often been suggested that Picasso's blue pictures reflect his own misery and poverty as an unsuccessful young painter in these early years. These works also belong to the *fin de siècle* world of symbolism, subjectivity, and sentiment.

BIBLIOGRAPHY: General reference: A. H. Barr, Jr., *Picasso, Fifty Years of His Art*, 1946.   *Lent by Mr. Lee A. Ault*

80.

HEAD OF A BOY

PABLO PICASSO (Spanish), born 1881.
Gouache on paper; 15 x 10".

In this powerfully stark head of a youth, the inward expressiveness and averted eyes suggest the sentiments of Picasso's earlier blue and rose paintings, while the harsh angularities and blunt constructive masses of the face presage the formal distortions of early Cubism. Painted in 1906, a landmark year in Picasso's career, this work, like many others, announces the artist's rigorous concentration on the purely constructive aspects of painting figures in space. The heavy outlining of the features, the opaque density of the space, and the exacting breakdown of the face and background into lighted and shadowed planes without transitional modeling culminate in the extraordinary deformations of Picasso's first pictorial manifesto, *Les Demoiselles d'Avignon* of 1907.

BIBLIOGRAPHY: C. Zervos, *Pablo Picasso, 1895-1906*, p. 155, fig. 331 and *Supplement*,
p. 95, No. 781.   *Lent by Mr. Lee A. Ault*

81.

SEATED WOMAN

PABLO PICASSO (Spanish), born 1881.
Oil on wood; 29¼ x 20⅝".

EXHIBITIONS: *Picasso, An American Tribute*, Perls Gallery, April 25-May 12, 1962, No. 6; *Picasso and Man*, Art Gallery of Toronto and Montreal Museum of Fine Arts, Jan. 11-March 31, 1964, No. 108; *Picasso*, Forth Worth Art Center Museum and Dallas Museum of Fine Arts, Feb. 8-March 26, 1967, No. 54.

The *Seated Woman* (1932), executed in an austere Synthetic Cubist style, is an elusive image of femininity. The ambiguity of the Cubist space heightens the mystery that is evoked by the juxtaposition of formal and emotional antitheses. Sensuous curving lines are set against more rigid vertical ones. The form itself is closed, as if protecting itself from the environment. The gently watchful female presence at the left is joined to her suspicious, brooding counterpart at the right. The drama between these opposing aspects of the woman's personality, as well as between the formal configurations, is stilled — and even partially denied — by the gray tones of the painting.

BIBLIOGRAPHY: A. H. Barr, Jr. *Picasso: Fifty Years of his Art*, 1946, p. 176; C. Zervos, *Pablo Picasso*, 1955, No. 405; R. Rosenblum, "Picasso as Surrealist," *Art Forum*, V (Sept. 1966) p. 23.   *Lent by Mr. Lee A. Ault*

82.
OWL
PABLO PICASSO (Spanish), born 1881.
Painted terracotta; height 13½″.

Thanks to the recent show of Picasso's sculpture at the Museum of Modern Art in New York, we have been given the opportunity to re-evaluate this aspect of Picasso's work. In the past, his sculpture has been perfunctorily dealt with as a further extension of ideas already developed in painting.

In this painted terracotta owl (1950), the flat staring face with bulbous multicolored eyes, the brightly patterned spots of paint, and the coarse modeling and equally crude application of paint work together to convey an emotional directness and a formal simplicity that remind us of Picasso's particular interest in the naiveté and freshness of a child's vision.

BIBLIOGRAPHY: D. H. Kahnweiler, *Picasso: Keramik*, 1957.   *Lent by Mr. Lee A. Ault*

83.
PLATE WITH FAUN AND OWL
PABLO PICASSO (Spanish), born 1881.
Ceramic; diameter 16½″.

In 1947, when Picasso began to make ceramics, he seemed to consider it a casual pastime. He was apparently attracted by the idea of making objects that could serve a practical purpose and be appreciated by a broader audience than his painting had found. However, within a few years, he had begun to treat the pottery less as a utilitarian object and more as a new artistic challenge, as can be seen in this ceramic plate made in 1957. The mood of playfulness, the childlike simplification of forms, and the spatial ambiguity (note how the design reads as if it were painted on a surface that is simultaneously flat and curved) are all typical of Picasso's style. At the same time, however, the plate exemplifies the traditional pottery aesthetic: figurative forms and painting technique reiterate the shape and texture of the plate itself.

Lent by Mr. Lee A. Ault

84.
WOMAN READING
ÉDOUARD VUILLARD (French), 1868-1940.
Tempera on canvas; 12 x 9″.

Vuillard was primarily a painter of interiors — comfortable, lived-in rooms usually graced by the unobtrusive presence of one or two people. The subjects of these paintings are the rooms themselves and not, as one might expect, what is happening in them. In *Woman Reading*, Vuillard emphatically states his interest in the room's atmosphere by placing the woman off to the left and focusing on the bedroom furnishings. He unites the two, however, through the redness of his palette and the overall surface patterning of gently swelling curves that contrast with hard right angles.

As a young man, Vuillard had been a member of the Nabis, a group of painters strongly influenced by Gauguin and his aesthetic theories. This work shows the influence of the Nabis in its elimination of extraneous detail and concentration on the expressive capacities of color, shape, and space. But the intimate subject and richly painted surface can be compared with works by Degas and the Impressionists.

BIBLIOGRAPHY: M. Raynal, *The History of Modern Painting from Baudelaire to Bonnard*, 1949, p. 99.

Lent by Mr. Lee A. Ault

85.
SAILBOATS AT COLLIOURE
ANDRÉ DERAIN (French), 1880-1954.
Oil on canvas; 25¾ x 32".

EXHIBITIONS: *Franse landschappen van Cézanne tot heden,* Museum Boymans-Van Beuningen, Rotterdam, 1963, No. 33; *Torso—das Unvollendete als künstlerische Form,* Kunsthalle, Recklinghausen, 1964, No. 269; *Les Fauves,* Tokyo, 1965, No. 14; *Autour de l'Impressionisme,* Galarie Beyeler, Basel, 1966, No. 15.

In 1905 Derain, Matisse, Rouault, and Vlaminck were unsympathetically dubbed "fauves," or wild beasts. Undoubtedly, it was the frenetic energy, arbitrary color, and free distortion of form which outraged the sensibilities of their contemporaries. The literal subject matter of *Sailboats at Collioure* (1905), an example of Fauve work, serves only as a point of departure for the staccato brushstrokes of intensely colored paint which form an agitated pattern on the surface of the canvas.

BIBLIOGRAPHY: G. Hilaire, *Derain,* 1959, pl. 38.

Lent by Mr. Charles W. Engelhard

86.
NUDE STANDING
GEORGES ROUAULT (French), 1871-1958.
Oil and gouache on paper; 17 x 10½".

Rouault was the most atypical member of the Fauve group. While Matisse, Derain, and Vlaminck often expressed exuberance and gaiety in their paintings, Rouault looked to the somber side of life. Following in the tradition of Goya and Daumier, he painted the outcasts of society, particularly clowns and prostitutes. A group of these works caused a sensation when they were first publicly exhibited at the Salon d'Automne in 1905.

In this painting (signed and dated 1905), color — the principal expressive device in Fauve painting — is handled with notable sensitivity, and the ostensibly sordid subject is transformed and dignified.

BIBLIOGRAPHY: General reference: P. Courthion, *Georges Rouault* (no date);
J. T. Soby, *Georges Rouault,* 1945.

Lent by Mr. Lee A. Ault

87.

GIRL WITH A HAT

HENRY MATISSE (French), 1869-1954.
Oil on canvas; 28 x 24".

EXHIBITIONS: *Henri Matisse*, Galerie Thannhauser, Berlin, 1930, No. 45; *Henri Matisse*, Museum of Modern Art, New York, 1931, No. 45; *French Painting from the 15th Century to the Present Day*, California Palace of the Legion of Honor, San Francisco, 1934; *Henri Matisse*, Boston Museum of Fine Arts and University of California at Los Angeles Art Council, 1966, No. 54.

Matisse once said, "Expression . . . does not consist of the passion mirrored upon a human face or betrayed by a violent gesture. The whole arrangement of my picture is expressive. . . ." This painting is a fine example of Matisse's words and fulfilled intentions. The girl's face, straightforwardly and simply rendered, remains passive as her bonnet comes alive and trumpets the two main themes of the painting: richly curving lines and decorative, lusciously colored blossoms. The voluptuous curve of the hat's crown and rim echoes throughout the painting; and the blossoms metamorphose magically into elegant meanders and arabesques. As Matisse intended, the whole arrangement of *Girl with a Hat* (1920) is indeed expressive.

Lent by Mr. Lee A. Ault

88.

SELF PORTRAIT

ROGER DE LA FRESNAYE (French), 1885-1925.
Pencil; 10¼ x 7⅝".

This self portrait is one of several from La Fresnaye's post-Cubist period. It was executed in 1920, probably during a period of illness. Prior to the First World War, which interrupted his career, the artist was associated with the *Section d'Or* Cubists; after the War, his work leaned strongly toward earlier pictorial traditions. The simplification of planes and the absolute reduction of pictorial elements to line and shading reflect his earlier contact with Cubism, but the modeling of the surfaces and the expressive eyes emphasize more traditional concerns. The elongation of the face and the hand denote his pensive inwardness and sensitivity, while the soft curves and lightly shaded areas suggest the passivity caused by his weakened physical condition. The faintly smiling visage shows self-awareness, as well as La Fresnaye's ability to express his physically impaired but mentally acute state.

BIBLIOGRAPHY: General reference: E. Nebelthau, *Roger de la Fresnaye*, 1935; R. Cogniat and W. George, *Oeuvre complète de Roger de la Fresnaye*, 1950; R. Rosenblum, *Cubism and Twentieth-Century Art*, 1966.

Lent by Professor and Mrs. E. Dudley H. Johnson

89.

WOMAN WITH MANDOLIN

GEORGES BRAQUE (French), 1882-1956.
Oil on canvas; 46 x 35".

The Cubist vocabulary of *Woman with Mandolin*, executed in 1931, recalls that of the years 1913-15, the formative period of Synthetic Cubism. The shaded, monotonously colored facets of the earlier Analytic Cubist works have here grown into large and decorative forms, gaily colored and variously textured. The viewer need not search far to discover a woman and a mandolin, although it may be difficult to relate specific forms to specific narrative details. The uncertainty is increased by the ambiguous definition of forms in space that is peculiar to Cubism. This can be observed, for instance, in the woman's right arm, which wends its way from background to foreground. It is the intention of Cubism to disorient the spectator in that manner, i.e., figurative details lose their specific identity in order to become part of a generalized pictorial image that is important in and of itself.

Lent by Mr. Lee A. Ault

90.
LA LUMIÈRE DE L'OMBRE
YVES TANGUY (French), 1900-1955.
Oil on canvas; 25⅜ x 20⅞".

Yves Tanguy was a member of André Breton's circle which initiated and led the Surrealist movement. *La Lumière de L'Ombre* (1939), a typical Surrealist "dreamscape," sometimes called a "landscape of the soul," is supposed to connote a psycho-cerebral world which exists beyond the limits of our daily experiences. The attention to detail and realistic rendering of surfaces suggest that the artist has painted the scene exactly as he "saw" it. The black shadows, however, are almost more tangible than the curiously shaped and textured objects which cast them. In the foreground, a straight, taut rope casts a wavy, slack shadow. Furthermore, the lucid clear light which defines and declares the absolute reality of the "dreamscape" fades into a background that has no horizon. Tanguy depicts the contradictions and uncertainties inherent in imaginative and visionary experiences.

BIBLIOGRAPHY: A. Breton, *Le surrealisme et la peinture*, 1928; J. T. Soby, *Yves Tanguy*, 1955.

Lent by Mr. Hugh J. Chisholm, Jr.

91.
THE GATEKEEPER'S PRIDE
PAUL KLEE (Swiss), 1879-1940.
Watercolor; 20 x 13".

The Gatekeeper's Pride (1929), like most of Klee's other paintings, is misleadingly simple in appearance. It is, however, the product of extraordinary intellectual control and concentration; for Klee, in this respect similar to the Surrealists, tried to find an objective vocabulary that could express the most intimate subconscious experiences. If we recognize this gatekeeper who seems more specter than human, it is because such a hieratic image is part of our own dream vocabulary. The use of geometrically solid forms with hazy edges, the elimination of narrative detail, and the creation of a space that is both infinite and flat are some of the formal means through which the artist's childlike vision of a quiet but imperious presence is conveyed.

BIBLIOGRAPHY: W. Grohmann, *Paul Klee*, 1954; W. Haftmann, *The Inward Vision: Watercolors, Drawings, and Writings by Paul Klee*, 1958.

Lent by Mr. Lee A. Ault

92.
GRAND NU JAUNE
MARC CHAGALL (Russian), born 1887.
Oil on canvas; 45½ x 38".

EXHIBITIONS: *Chagall*, Galerie Maeght, Paris, March-April 1950, No. 2; *Recent Paintings by Chagall*, M. Knoedler and Co., N.Y., April 16-May 5, 1951, No. 3.

Chagall's world is one of fantasy. His images are gathered from his memories of the past and his nostalgia for a simple pure life. Unlike the Surrealists, whose nightmarish worlds are also evoked by memory images, Chagall's paintings are always happy — wishful thoughts and pleasant day-dreams.

This painting, signed and dated 1949, is pervaded by a memory of primeval lushness and well-being as figures float miraculously in space, suspended it seems, by their own blithe spirits. Fertility is the *leitmotif* seen in the spilling forth of flowers, the piling up of fruit, and in the modest but full-bodied nudity of the woman with child. As man, woman, and child affectionately touch one another, angels make joyful music in celebration of this festival of birth.

BIBLIOGRAPHY: F. Meyer, *Marc Chagall, Leben und Werk*, 1961, fig. 794.   *Lent by Mr. Hugo V. Neuhaus, Jr.*

93.
WEST SIDE DOCKS
GEORGE LUKS (American), 1867-1933.
Oil; 21 x 27″ (with frame).

EXHIBITIONS: *Exhibition of the Works of George B. Luks*, Worcester Art Museum and Newark Museum, 1934, No. 13.

George Luks, a member of the Ashcan School of Painting, was one of "The Eight" who revolted against approved academic standards in order to depict the specifically American life in an American style. The desire to represent the daily life of the metropolis was a radical departure in subject matter. Luks had studied at the Pennsylvania Academy of Fine Arts, where he absorbed the realism of Thomas Eakins. He augmented this with a simplification of style in rendering the human form which is shown in separate masses of lights and darks. The *West Side Docks* was painted in 1905.

BIBLIOGRAPHY: E. L. Cary, *George Luks*, 1931; M. Brown, *American Painting from the Armory Show to the Depression*, 1955.   *Lent by Mr. Roderick H. Cushman*

94.
EARLY EVENING
MAURICE BRAZIL PRENDERGAST (American), 1859-1924.
Oil on panel; 15 x 24″.

EXHIBITIONS: *Maurice Prendergast*, Museum of Fine Arts, Boston, October 26-December 4, 1960, No. 42.

When Maurice Prendergast studied in Paris in 1891-94, he came into contact with the works of the most advanced French artists — Cézanne, Seurat, and Gauguin — who influenced him in the development of his own expressive variant of the Post-Impressionist style, a style novel to American art. In panoramic compositions such as *Early Evening*, executed c.1917-20, Prendergast depicted outdoor scenes of crowds at their leisure as a series of shapes and hues far removed from any naturalistic limitations imposed by the real world. Indeed, when he exhibited with "The Eight" in 1908, a critic called his works "an explosion in a color factory."

Lent by Mr. Roderick H. Cushman

95.
NEW ENGLAND HOUSES
CHARLES DEMUTH (American), 1883-1935.
Watercolor on white paper; 10 x 13″.

EXHIBITIONS: *Centennial Loan Exhibition*, Vassar College, 1961, No. 127.

Demuth evolved his own aristocratic and elegant Expressionism on the basis of his admiration for

Duchamp and the Cubists. His fastidious pencil and watercolor technique and his wonderfully delicate use of wash combined with his sinister and tortuous use of line to form one of the most moving styles in 20th-century American art. *New England Houses* is signed and dated 1918.

Lent by Mr. Benjamin Rowland, Jr.

96.
MAPLES IN AUTUMN FOLIAGE
JOHN MARIN (American), 1870-1953.
Watercolor; 15 x 19¾".

EXHIBITIONS: Gallery of Contemporary Art, Toronto, October 1956; *Philadelphia Collects: 20th Century*, Oct. 2-Nov. 17, 1963.

Maples in Autumn Foliage (signed and dated 1949) is a relatively late work in Marin's career. It exhibits tendencies that can be traced back to his *Woolworth Building* (1912) and his *Maine Islands* (1922). This watercolor, in its reduction of compositional elements to brushstrokes, spots, and dabs, exemplifies Marin's type of American Cubism. These raw forms provide axes of movement that contrast and collide with each other to create an overall unifying dynamism.

BIBLIOGRAPHY: *John Marin: A Retrospective Exhibition* (catalogue of exhibition at the
Institute of Modern Art, Boston), 1947; W. C. Williams, D. Phillips,
et al., John Marin, 1956.
Lent by Mr. and Mrs. William P. Wood

97.
ABSTRACT PAINTING, UNTITLED
MARK ROTHKO (American), born 1903.
Oil on canvas; 61¼ x 46¾".

In 1935 Mark Rothko and Adolph Gottlieb co-founded "The Ten," an Expressionist-oriented group which was associated with the W. P. A. Federal Arts Project in New York in 1936-37, and which exhibited works influenced by Surrealism at the Art of This Century Gallery. By 1947 Rothko had begun to eliminate biomorphic elements from his paintings; and in 1950 his painting style was characterized by rectangular fields of diffusing color. Rothko, a proponent of "quietistic" abstraction, here achieves his ends through the use of soft-edge transitions and dissolution of outlines. These produce an impression of the absence of weight that gives the painting an elusive, intangible quality. The painting was executed in 1951.

BIBLIOGRAPHY: General reference: A. Pellegrini, *New Tendencies in Art*, 1960; N. Ponents,
Contemporary Trends, 1960; P. Selz, *Mark Rothko* (catalogue of exhibition at The Museum
of Modern Art, New York), 1961.
Anonymous Loan

98.
CITIZEN CLARK
ANDREW WYETH (American), born 1917.
Tempera 14⅜ x 22¾".

EXHIBITIONS: *Andrew Wyeth, Recent Paintings*, M. Knoedler and Co., New York, Oct. 28-Nov. 22, 1958, No. 43; *Andrew Wyeth, Temperas, Water Colors and Drawings*, Albright-Knox Art Gallery, Buffalo, Nov. 2-Dec. 9, 1962, No. 118; *Andrew Wyeth*, Pennsylvania Academy, 1966, No. 108.

Wyeth's portrayal of American life as well as his realistic style place him in the main stream of American Realism along with such men as Eakins, Homer, and Hopper.

Citizen Clark (1957) typifies Wyeth's preoccupation with the indiscriminate passage of time. Clark and the room he inhabits have weathered the years, and both bear marks of time's passing. In the left corner a calendar reiterates this theme, and even the composition, as it rushes quickly off to the right — hurried along by white highlights, Clark's placement off center to the right, and his gaze in that direction beyond the picture's edge — restates this motif. The spare austerity of setting, the intensity of closely scrutinized details, and the high-pitched drama of light patterns all lend an almost hallucinatory character to this painting.

BIBLIOGRAPHY: M. S. Young, "Wyeth and Manet in Philadelphia,"*APOLLO* (Nov. 1966) p. 404; R. Meryman, *Andrew Wyeth*, 1968.

Lent by Mr. Alexander M. Laughlin

99.
UNTITLED: STRIPE SERIES
MORRIS LOUIS (American), 1912-1962.
Acrylic on canvas; 84 x 48″.

Morris Louis, the foremost painter in the "Washington Color School" until his untimely death in 1962, painted in an Expressionist manner until 1951. At that time, he came to New York and was exposed to the work of Jackson Pollock and Helen Frankenthaler. He was especially intrigued by the staining technique used by the latter in her *Mountains and Sea*. Upon his return to Washington he began to concentrate on color-field painting and was one of the first artists to use Bocour "Magna," a now well-known synthetic acrylic paint. Louis executed the so-called stripe paintings in 1961-62. Each stripe is stained into the raw canvas, identifying paint with ground. The colors are integrated through their similar hues and equal intensities, though each also retains its own searing, individual intensity. This particular canvas (1961) is a fine example of Louis' ability to free color from other pictorial associations.

BIBLIOGRAPHY: *Morris Louis 1912-1962* (catalogue of exhibition at the Museum of Fine Arts, Boston), 1967 (contains bibliography).

Anonymous Loan

100.
BREAD AND CLOTH
WALTER MURCH (Canadian, naturalized American), 1907-1967.
Oil on canvas; 28¼ x 22¼″.

EXHIBITIONS: *Walter Murch*, Betty Parsons Gallery, New York, 1966, No. 1; *Recent Still Life*, Rhode Island Museum of Art, School of Design, Providence, 1966, No. 49; *Walter Murch, Retrospective Exhibition*, Rhode Island Museum of Art, School of Design, Providence, Nov. 9-Dec. 4, 1966, No. 66.

An airy, misty atmosphere surrounds a loaf of bread that radiates an aura of light — a gentle, lyrical light that clouds the physical boundaries of the object as it disintegrates and unites with the enveloping void. Indeed, Murch has stated: "I see the air between the apple and my eye. I see what air does to apples." *Bread and Cloth* was executed in 1965.

BIBLIOGRAPHY: C. Gary, "Walter Murch, Modern Alchemist," *Art in America*, LI (1963); R. Browne, "Short Range Astronomy," *Art News*, 64 (1966).

Lent by Mr. Lee A. Ault

ORIENTAL ART

INTRODUCTION: Oriental Art

Miniature paintings from Iran, Turkey, and India provide some of the most exciting experiences in the world of art. While the majority of these small pictures might be considered visual *bonbons,* the best of them are profoundly rewarding. The present exhibition offers a splendid sampling of their pleasures.

Although all of these pictures are linked by belonging to different phases of a widespread tradition, they are nevertheless extremely varied. The Iranian miniatures, such as the magnificent selection from Mr. Arthur Houghton's *Shahnama* — one of the world's greatest manuscripts — were created for the powerful and sophisticated Shah Tahmasb of the Safavid dynasty, a prince who could command a small army of craftsmen and artists to produce a volume of unrivaled sumptuousness. Other miniatures, such as those from the Hindu Rajput courts, were created for humbler men whose interest in art, however, was no less intense.

These paintings are all small in size. They had to be portable, as patrons and artists were often on the move. Wall paintings also existed to adorn palaces, forts, or baths; but the more characteristic format was the illustrated book or album, or — in India — the stack of pictures wrapped in a cloth. These are intimate works of arts and were not intended to be put behind glass and hung on walls. Rather, they should be held in the hand, so that their glistening gold can catch the light. Many were illustrations for books: volumes of verse, religious texts, or histories. They are all painted on paper in a medium comparable to opaque watercolor. The craft was complex. Artists began their training as young children and did not achieve mastery until they neared twenty. Motifs were passed on from one generation to the next; and artists' families or workshops handed down "recipe books" containing figures, animals, trees, etc. to be traced by successive generations. Geniuses saw the world afresh and invented new forms; less imaginative artists repeated the old ones.

Despite the social, historical, and chronological distance which separates us from these works, they are still meaningful for us today. We can approach them from many levels. Specialists can quibble over dates, provenances, and attributions; but far more satisfying is the ostensibly easier — but in fact far rarer — approach: that of the viewer with an innocently open eye.

S. C. Welch, Jr.

101.

BIZHAN RIDDING THE LAND OF THE WILD BOAR
Iran; Mongol period, 14th century.
Miniature painting; 4¾ x 2".

This painting is from a small manuscript of the *Shahnama*. The artist has emphasized Bizhan's strength by distorting the size of his shoulders and arms, and by painting him disproportionately larger in scale than his surroundings. The surging movement of the horse and the spreading branches of the trees, together with the contortions of the dying animals, lend an unusual vitality to the composition.

BIBLIOGRAPHY: E. Grube, *Muslim Miniature Paintings*, 1962, No. 16.   *Lent by Mr. Stuart C. Welch, Jr.*

102.

THE HOUGHTON *SHAHNAMA*
Iran; Safavid Dynasty, c.1520-1540.
Miniature painting; folio size 18½ x 12⅝", text area size 10½ x 6¹¹⁄₁₆".

EXHIBITIONS: Paris, 1903 (lent by the Rothschild family); Grolier Club, New York, 1962 (lent by Arthur A. Houghton, Jr.).

This exhibition includes six folios — five miniatures and an illuminated rosette — from the great *Shahnama (The Book of Kings)* manuscript prepared by the royal workshops for Shah Tahmasb (1524-76), the second ruler of the Safavid Dynasty. Although there is no colophon or scribe's name in the volume, one miniature is dated the equivalent of 1527. On stylistic grounds, 258 miniatures of this generously illustrated copy of the Iranian national epic, which was gathered together and put into literary form by the poet Firdowsi, can be dated from the early 1520s through the latter part of the 1530s. In its pages can be traced the development of the Safavid style from the years immediately preceding the reign of Shah Tahmasb through the period just before the creation of the great Nizami manuscript in the British Museum (Or. 2265; see Binyon, *The Poems of Nizami*, 1928). The earliest miniatures are characteristic of the period of Shah Isma'il, when Sultan-Muhammad was still painting in the Turkman tradition of Tabriz (folio 21 verso). Later miniatures, such as *The Death of Zahhak* (folio 37 verso), reveal the same artist's work after his earlier style had been synthesized with the less ecstatic and more logical polished manner brought to Tabriz from Herat by the great master of the Timurid period, Bihzad, who probably came to the capital with Prince Tahmasb in 1522.

Although the manuscript contains only two signed miniatures (one of these, by Dust-Muhammad, was added after the completion of the project), it has been possible on stylistic grounds to assign the pictures to many of the leading masters of the royal atelier: Sultan-Muhammad, Mir Musavvir, Aqa-Mirak, Dust-Muhammad, Mirza 'Ali, Mir Sayyid 'Ali, Muzaffar 'Ali, Shaykh Muhammad, and Abd ul Samad. The hands of six lesser masters can also be identified, although their names remain questionable.

Little is known of the history of the manuscript, which contains no owners' seals or comments. An opening rosette (folio 16 recto) lists the names and titles of the patron, Shah Tahmasb. Protective leaves over each of the miniatures contain synopses of the subjects illustrated; these synopses were written in 1800 by a royal librarian at the Ottoman court.

102a.
16 recto — ROSETTE

The rosette is inscribed: "Commissioned for the Royal Library of the most mighty Sultan, and the most just and beneficent Khaqan (Grand Khan), sultan, son and grandson of sultans, Abu'l-Muzaffar (The Victorious), Sultan Shah Tahmasb, of Husayni and Safavid descent, Bahadur (The Valiant) Khan. May God, the Most Exalted, perpetuate his realm and his rule, and diffuse [lower cartouche] his justice and his benevolence throughout the world."

102b.
21 verso — HUSHANG SLAYS THE BLACK DIV
Attributed to Sultan-Muhammad.

Hushang was ordered by his grandfather, the legendary first king of Iran and of the world, to wage a holy war against the forces of evil represented by the Black Div, or Devil. Here, in this wildly funny yet profoundly serious picture— one of the earliest miniatures for the project — the hero is shown as demon-slayer, assisted by an army of animals and angels. In style, the picture is still markedly Turkman. The divs, animals, landscape, and figures emerge directly from the world represented in an album now in Istanbul (H. 2153, Topkapu Sarayi Museum Library); according to tradition (probably correct), the Istanbul album belonged to Yaqub Beq, a leading patron of the Aq-Qoyunlu Turkmans at Tabriz. Although there is no evidence that Sultan Muhammad grew up here, his early style was strongly influenced by Tabriz material, much of which probably fell into Safavid hands along with the spoils of that capital.

102c.
37 verso — THE DEATH OF ZAHHAK
Attributed to Sultan-Muhammad.

The tyrant Zahhak was bedeviled through his own ambition into helping to slay his father. Later, because of his greed, snakes sprouted from his shoulders; these monsters required daily meals of human brains. Finally, his people, led by Faridun, revolted. Here, the hero supervises the chaining of the tyrant to Mount Damavand, where he was to be left that "his brain might chafe and his agony endure." In this miniature, Sultan-Muhammad's earlier style is fully synthesized with the less robust, more "classical" idiom of Bihzad: the naturalistic refinements attained in Timurid Herat have been incorporated. The grotesque demons depicted in folio 21 verso have here become virtual house-pets and courtiers. We are but a step removed from Sultan-Muhammad's contributions to the Nizami manuscript of 1539-43.

102d.
62 verso — ZAL IS SIGHTED BY A CARAVAN
Attributed to Painter D.

Zal, born an albino, was exposed on a mountain by his distraught father, Sam. Fortunately, he was cared for by God, through His agent, a huge bird known as the Simurgh. In time, the white-haired youth was sighted by a caravan, which brought word of the boy's survival to Sam, who came for him. Zal eventually became king. This miniature can be ascribed to one of Sultan-Muhammad's followers whom we have called Painted D and who painted many miniatures for the *Shahnama*. Here, although all of the actual painting is by Painter D, he probably worked closely with the master, who may well have sketched in the design.

102e.
67 verso — ZAL ENTERTAINS MIHRAB AT KABUL
Attributed to Mir Musavvir.

Zal's romance with Rudabe, the daughter of Mihrab, provides one of the central themes of the *Shahnama*. Here, the plot begins with the bridegroom-to-be meeting his future father-in-law.

Mir Musavvir, along with Sultan-Muhammad and Aqa-Mirak, was a senior artist of the project. Until recently, his only known inscribed work was a portrait in the British Museum. On the basis of this portrait, a considerable group of miniatures was attributed to the master. Happily, a tiny inscription on one of the miniatures that had been assigned to him on stylistic grounds has come to light recently: it is his own signature. The master's style is dignified, deliberate, and exceptionally pleasing. Although he lacks Sultan-Muhammad's visionary power and brilliance, his mellifluous line, harmonious color, and gentle lyricism raise him to the front ranks of Iranian painters.

102f.
110 verso — RUSTAM BEFORE KAY QUBAD
Attributed to Aqa-Mirak.

When Iran was invaded by Afrasiyab the Turanian, a Shah had to be found to replace the extinct line of Pishdadi. Rustam, the greatest hero of Iran, was dispatched to seek out Kay Qubad, a descendant of Faridun, who had been recommended by one of the magi. At last, under magical circumstances, Rustam discovered the young man enthroned near a river bank at the foot of Mount Alburz. After drinking a toast "To the Free," Rustam and his new Shah rode off together to the vacant throne of Iran. Here, Aqa-Mirak has set before us a refulgent, sunny day, and a festive gathering of elegant courtiers. On grounds of style, it can be seen that he painted this miniature during the later years of the *Shahnama* project.

BIBLIOGRAPHY: E. Blochet, "Mussulman Manuscripts and Miniatures as illustrated in the recent exhibition at Paris," *Burlington Magazine*, II (June 1903) pp. 132-44, pl. 3; F. R. Martin, *The Miniature Painting and Painters of Persia, India and Turkey*, 1912, II, pls. 122-29; G. Migeon, *Manuel d'art musulman*, 2nd ed., 1927, I, fig. 48; I. V. Stchoukine, *Les peintures des manuscrits safavis*, 1959, pp. 65-68. The entire manuscript is soon to be published by the Harvard University Press, along with a study of the historical background, monographs on the artists, and an account of Safavid painting with respect to the Turko-Iranian tradition. This project is the cooperative work of Professor Martin Bernard Dickson of Princeton University and Mr. Stuart C. Welch, Jr. of the Fogg Art Museum, Harvard University.

Lent by Mr. Arthur A. Houghton, Jr.

103.

GABRIEL ANNOUNCING THE APOTHEOSIS OF 'ALI
From a copy of the *Khavarnama* of Ibn Husam.
Iran; c.1450-1477.
Miniature painting; 9⅜ x 4⅝".

This work is from a copy of the *Khavarnama* of Ibn Husam, a manuscript containing several dates ranging from 1450 to 1477. The text is of Shiah origin and describes episodes in the life of 'Ali, the son-in-law of the Prophet. The painting seems to have been made under Turkman patronage, although the place of origin is not certain. Its style combines Tabriz decorative motifs — especially in the vegetation — and elements associated with centers such as Shiraz, where commercial workshops turned out large numbers of illustrated manuscripts, mostly for distribution to sub-royal patrons.

BIBLIOGRAPHY: B. Gray, *Persian Painting*, 1961, pp. 104-6, pl. p. 107; E. Grube, *Muslim Miniature Paintings*, 1962, No. 49.

Lent by Mr. Stuart C. Welch, Jr.

104.

THE CELEBRATION OF 'ID
SULTAN-MUHAMMAD (Persian), 16th century.
Miniature painting; 9⅞ x 5⅞".

The only two signed pictures by the great master Sultan-Muhammad (see also No. 102) are contained in the *Divan* of Hafiz, a manuscript of poetry. Although undated, the manuscript bears a close resemblance to a royal copy, dated 1526-27, of the collected works of Mir Ali Shir Nawa'i (Paris, Bibliothèque Nationale, Sup. turc 316).

This painting depicts the feast of 'Id, which marks the end of the fast of Ramadan. The artist has turned an amused eye upon the foibles of a wordly court, aptly illustrating the poet's verse. Above the archway an inscription reads: "Al-Ghazi Abu'l-Muzaffar Sam Mirza," a reference to the brother of the Safavid Shah, Shah Tahmasb, in whose workshop at Tabriz the manuscript was prepared, perhaps as a present from the ruler to his brother.

BIBLIOGRAPHY: A. U. Pope, ed., *A Survey of Persian Art*, 1938, V, p. 900.

Lent by Mr. Stuart C. Welch, Jr.

105.

YOUTH WITH WINE CUP
Iran; 1560-1570.
Attributed to Mirza 'Ali.
Miniature painting; 4½ x 2⅜".

This characteristically idealized portrait, the style of which invites comparison with European

Mannerism, can be ascribed to Mirza 'Ali, the son of Sultan-Muhammad. Although his early artistic career in the royal workshops of Tabriz in the 1520s was particularly influenced by the painter Shaykh Zadeh, he soon became a notable master. His work combined the anecdotal vitality of his father's idiom with the exquisite fineness and spacial logic of Bihzad's Herat style. As he grew older, his painting became increasingly free and "baroque." The miniature at hand can be seen as transitional between the later stages of the school of Shah Tahmasb and the period of Shah Abbas. Its style already approaches those of Siyavush the Georgian, Sadiki Beq, and Aqa Riza, all of whom were strongly influenced by this leading master.

BIBLIOGRAPHY: E. Grube, *Muslim Miniature Paintings*, 1962, No. 93.   *Lent by Mr. Stuart C. Welch, Jr.*

106.
MAN AND MONKEY RIDING A NAG
Iran; c.1590.
Attributed to Siyavush the Georgian.
Tinted drawing; 4¹⁄₁₆ x 4⅛″.

At its most profound, as in this tinted drawing, Persian painting evokes the mystical spirit of Sufism. Here, the monkey is more human than the man; and the horse, happily resigned though emaciated, seems wiser than either. The artist's calligraphically controlled brushwork, reminiscent of *nastaliq* script, surpasses virtuosity. Siyavush the Georgian, to whom this picture has been ascribed by B. W. Robinson in a letter to the owner, was a slave boy whose talent earned him a place in Shah Tahmasb's ateliers. By 1590 he had become one of the leading artists of Iran.

BIBLIOGRAPHY: A. Sakisian, *La miniature persane*, 1929, fig. 107.   *Lent by Mr. Stuart C. Welch, Jr.*

107.
ALBUM PAGE
Iran; Safavid period, 16th century.
Written by Mir Ali al-Katib.
Calligraphy; text area 7⅞ x 4⅞″.

A major scribe such as Mir Ali, who had worked for the Timurid dynasty prior to his employment at the Safavid court, was at least as much admired as the greatest painters. Examples of his calligraphy were mounted in albums, often along with miniatures. Special craftsmen were responsible for assembling these glittering pages in which gold-flecked and tinted papers, passages of arabesque ornament, and the other ingredients were cut out and mounted together in subtle compositions. On the basis of the palette, arabesque, and writing, this folio can be dated to about 1530. Other folios from the same album are in the collection of Leland C. Wyman and the Fogg Art Museum, Cambridge.

Lent by Mr. Stuart C. Welch, Jr.

108.
FOLIO FROM A KORAN
Iran; Seljuk, 12th century.
Calligraphy; text area 9⅛ x 6⅜″.

This folio is from a scattered copy of the Koran, or sacred Moslem Book of the Prophet. A section of this manuscript has been preserved in Dublin at the Chester Beatty Library, while other folios are in museums and libraries in Europe and America. It should also be mentioned that a folio closely resembling this one is presently in the Metropolitan Museum of Art (formerly of the Havemeyer Collection).

The combined use of calligraphy and arabesque or floral patterns was a highly developed skill of Seljuk artists who raised the status of inscription from that of a mere task to an aesthetic experience. This early Islamic technique was not confined to manuscripts; it was also used on textiles, pottery, and metalwork. The contrast between the formal, angular lines of this variant Kufic script and the circular pattern of the background is emphasized by the stark color of the oversize letters against the subdued tints of the smaller floral design. The total effect, however, is one of harmony, balance, and subtle movement.

BIBLIOGRAPHY: M. S. Dimant, *A Handbook of Muhammadan Art,* 1944; Chester Beatty Library, Dublin, *Catalogue of Turkish Manuscripts...*, 1958, pl. 31.   *Lent by Mr. Stuart C. Welch, Jr.*

109.
DRAGON
Turkey or Iran; c.1560.
Signed: Mir Sayyid Muhammad naqqash ("the painter").
Tinted drawing, 6⅚₆ x 12⅟₁₆".

According to an inscription, this drawing was made for Nawwab Khan Ahmad al-Hassani, the ruler of Gilan, a principality bordering the Caspian Sea. During the late 15th century, the royal family of Gilan intermarried with the Turkman house centered at Tabriz. When the Safavid dynasty replaced the Turkmans, they too married daughters of the Gilan princes.

Stylistically, this lively picture recalls the Chinese motifs which had been so dramatically reinterpreted in Tabriz painting from the Mongol period onward. We are especially reminded of the dragons in the Turkman drawings gathered into an album for Yaqub Beq (Istanbul, Topkapu Sarayi Museum Library, H. 2153). These fantastic beasts might be considered the more urban ancestors of the one at hand; the latter retains a good measure of their vitality in spite of its late and provincial origin. It is intriguing to note the extremely close resemblance between this drawing and several large blue-and-white tiled panels in Istanbul at the Topkapu Sarayi Museum. Inasmuch as the Prince of Gilan, whose name is inscribed on our drawing, is known to have journeyed to the Ottoman capital in the 1560's, presumably with his artists, it seemed more than likely that his visit was responsible for the vogue for Turkman motifs that characterized much of Turkish art at this time.

BIBLIOGRAPHY: E. Grube, "Miniatures in Istanbul Libraries, 1," *Pantheon,* XX (1962) fig. 15; _____, *Muslim Miniature Paintings,* 1962, No. 76.   *Lent by Mr. Stuart C. Welch, Jr.*

110.
BATTLE SCENE
From a *Bhagavata Purana* series.
India (Rajasthan); Mewar(?), c.1540 or earlier.
Miniature painting; 7 x 9⅜".

EXHIBITIONS: *Gods, Thrones, and Peacocks,* Asia House, New York, 1965-66, p. 115, No. 3a.

According to the collector, this painting seems to be from a well-known set of illustrations for the *Bhagavata Purana,* a Hindu epic which consists of a group of legends concerning the god Vishnu in his various incarnations. This early Rajput painting involves the god and his followers in a battle scene similar to those which formed the main occupation of the Rajput princes.

The style of this illustration represents the Rajput tradition of western India prior to the adoption of the naturalism and more subtle color harmonies of the Mughal court painters. However, the impact of the Moslem rulers of Northern India is already evident in the arabesque ornament. In his depiction of this splendid battle, the artist has not been hindered by the use of perspective. He has mingled the bold important figures of the gods with the activities of lesser warriors and fighting animals. The golden, blue-headed chariots seem to glide against a brilliant background through a conscious mélange of vivid color, shape, and pattern. The dynamic vigor of this style is closely related to an earlier work from Central India, the *Durga* (see *Gods, Thrones, and Peacocks*, No. 1), the style of which is derived from late Hindu wall paintings.

Lent by Mr. Stuart C. Welch, Jr.

111.

KURSHIDCHEHR FREES HAMID
From the *Dastan i Amir Hamza (The Story of Hamza)*.
India; Mughal, c.1570.
Miniature painting, tempera on cotton; 26⁵⁄₁₆ x 20″.

EXHIBITIONS: S. C. Welch, "Early Mughal Miniature Paintings shown at the Fogg Art Museum," *Ars Orientalis*, III, fig. 1; *Gods, Thrones, and Peacocks*, Asia House, New York, 1965-66, fig. 4 and p. 116, No. 4.

The huge manuscript from which this page has survived was painted for the Mughal Emperor Akbar the Great (1557-1605) when his court was centered at Fatehpur-Sirkri. In style, it represents the synthesis of elements from foreign and local sources: from the Safavid mode of Tabriz, where the emperor's father, Humayun, had recruited several Safavid masters; and from the many Hindu and pre-Mughal sources within India itself. The centripetal power of the composition can be likened to the pulling together of the empire under the vigorous leadership of the emperor-patron, whose storyteller would hold up such pictures as this while reading the story from the text inscribed on the back. Although Mughal art was to gain in refinement, it would never again match this early stage in dynamism. This miniature can be compared with the Mughal lion (No. 124) in its combination of naturalistic observation and abstract patterning.

BIBLIOGRAPHY: General reference: H. Gluck, *Die indischen Miniaturen des Hamzae-Romanes*, 1925; R. Ettinghausen, *Paintings of the Sultans and Emperors of India in American Collections*, 1961.

Lent by Mr. Stuart C. Welch, Jr.

112.

A DERVISH AND A MUSICIAN
India; Mughal, c.1609.
Signed by Daulat.
Miniature painting; 5¼ x 3⁵⁄₁₆″.

EXHIBITIONS: *Gods, Thrones, and Peacocks*, Asia House, New York, 1965-66, No. 8.

The trend toward naturalism and the absorption of Persian Safavid traditions had begun at the court of Akbar but reached its maturity during the reign of his son, Jahangir. A fluid, sensitive line retained from pre-Mughal Indian art was combined with a new perceptive naturalism and subdued landscape to produce the highest achievements of Mughal art of the 17th century. The artist Daulat, who may have been influenced by European work at this time, was in part responsible for this development.

The figures in this scene are not merely illustrations for a manuscript but are psychological portraits of two men depicted in a tense interplay of emotion and response. A slight vein of satire and mockery is evident in this study of a misguided, self-tortured holy man and his evil musician companion. The naturalism of expression and the use of controlled line are enhanced by the soft retreat of the relatively open landscape in the background. The depth and vitality of the human figures are offset by the delicate rendering of the creatures and foliage patterns in the foreground.

Lent by Mr. Stuart C. Welch, Jr.

113.
RAMA AND LAKSHMAN CONVERSE WITH AN ASCETIC
Illustration for the *Ramayana*.
Central India; Malwa, c.1635.
Miniature painting; 7 x 9⅛".

EXHIBITIONS: *Rajput Painting*, Asia House, New York, 1960, No. 6.

Malwa, in the central half of western India, lies along the eastern border of Mewar, the center of Rajput Central Indian painting. The early Moslems had established a caliphate in this area, and Akbar later installed a Mughal governor; but Mewar and Malwa, unlike Rajasthan, remained conservatively Hindu and Rajput.

The evidence for the date and provenance of this illustration for the *Ramayana* is based upon the similar style in a dated set of Malwa illustrations for another Vaishnavite text, the *Rasikapriya*. Both texts are concerned with the Hindu god Vishnu; the *Rasikapriya* deals primarily with the love of Krishna and Radha, while the famous *Ramayana* contains the adventures of Rama, Vishnu's seventh incarnation.

Malwa paintings resemble those of Mewar in their sensitive stylization of landscape and animals combined with influences from earlier Sultanate sources. This illustration may contain some Mughal qualities in the arrangement of the figures, but the broad flat planes of the background, the intense colors, and the facial renderings are in an earlier tradition.

BIBLIOGRAPHY: General reference: W. G. Archer, *Central Indian Painting*, 1958; S. C. Welch and M. C. Beach, *Gods, Thrones, and Peacocks* (catalogue of exhibition at Asia House), 1965.
Lent by Mr. Stuart C. Welch, Jr.

114.
RAM SINGH OF KOTAH PURSUING A RHINOCEROS
India (Rajasthan); Kotah, c.1700.
Miniature painting; 19½ x 12".

EXHIBITIONS: *Rajput Painting*, Asia House, New York, 1960, No. 36; *Gods, Thrones, and Peacocks*, Asia House, 1965-66, No. 27.

When Shah Jehan granted independence to Kotah, formerly a part of Bundi, he succeeded in weakening the power of the Rajput princes. He also unwittingly created a great new school of Kotah Rajput painting. Kotah style owes much to earlier Bundi work, but the particular qualities which distinguish Kotah paintings have established this illustration as one of the finest examples of Rajput painting.

The school of Kotah is noted for its fine hunting scenes. Unlike Mughal works, in which attention is focused on the emperor or prince, the human figures of Ram Singh I (1676-1708) and his companion are relatively unobtrusive, though they are highlighted with brilliant color. The main object of attention, however, is the magnificent elephant that occupies the greater part of the painting. The lumbering body of the elephant is invested with remarkable swiftness by the controlled use of an exquisitely rendered outline and a subdued but powerful modeling. The treatment of the head and upper trunk is a masterpiece of artistry in the employment of shadow, line, and expression. The decorative patterns in this painting are also used to enhance activity, rather than to confine it. The artist is unkown, but the collector has rightfully observed that his works "earn him a place in the company of the greatest Persian and Mughal masters."

BIBLIOGRAPHY: General reference: W. G. Archer, *Indian Painting in Bundi and Kotah*, 1959.

Lent by Mr. Stuart C. Welch, Jr.

115.
KRISHNA FLUTING IN A WOOD
Central India, early 18th century.
Miniature painting; 11½ x 8¾".

EXHIBITIONS: *Rajput Painting*, Asia House, New York, 1960, No. 12.

The cult of Krishna and the gopi (cow-girl) Radha had enjoyed popularity throughout the latter part of the 17th century in the Hindu Rajput state of Mewar. When, in the early 18th century, this cult was adopted in Bundi, Mewar artistic techniques seem to have accompanied it.

This illustration shows the god playing his flute to attract the gopis who were his companions. The style of this later Rajput painting recalls the earlier work of Mewar and Malwa artists, but their sensitive, lively stylization of the intimate foliage has given way to a symmetrical patterning and an exaggerated rendering of plant forms. The stark, open expanse of the flat background and the subdued colors provide an impression of dead heat which is relieved only by the brilliance of the centrally placed Krishna.

BIBLIOGRAPHY: General reference: M. Chandra, *Mewar Painting*, 1957; W. G. Archer, *Central Indian Painting*, 1958; _____, *Indian Painting in Bundi and Kotah*, 1959.

Lent by Mr. Stuart C. Welch, Jr.

116.
THE MONTH OF MAGHA
From a *Baramasa* set.
India (Rajasthan); Bikaner, c.1720.
Attributed to Ustad Ahmad Murad.
Miniature painting; 10⅜ x 7".

EXHIBITIONS: *Rajput Painting*, Asia House, New York, 1960, No. 43.

A *Baramasa* series consists of twelve miniatures, each representing a month. In this case, the lover and his beloved — the usual subject of the series — are depicted exchanging a flower that has been poetically transformed into a voluptuous red curtain.

The artist, a Moslem, painted this miniature in his old age. It is the work of a painter whose spirit has transformed technique. A signed and dated portrait of the prince who is shown here (Zorawar Singh) is clearly by the same hand (see Goetz, fig. 88). Another page from this set has been published in *Gods, Thrones, and Peacocks*, No. 30 (see bibliography).

BIBLIOGRAPHY: General reference: H. Goetz, *The Art and Architecture of Bikaner State*, 1950; B. Gray, *Treasures of Indian Miniatures in the Bikaner Palace Collection*, 1951; S. C. Welch and M. C. Beach, *Gods, Thrones, and Peacocks* (catalogue of exhibition at Asia House), 1965.   *Lent by Mr. Stuart C. Welch, Jr.*

117.

PORTRAIT OF TRILOKHA KHATRI AS A BRIDEGROOM

India (Rajasthan) ; Bikaner, c.1725.
Miniature painting; 4⅜ x 4″.

EXHIBITIONS: *Rajput Painting*, Asia House, New York, 1960, No. 44.

The hint of mockery and human weakness in the Mughal painting, *A Dervish and a Musician* (No. 112), appears full-blown in this Rajput portrait which owes much to the naturalism and perception of the Mughal painter Daulat. On the other hand, the incisive powerful lines of this work are purely Rajput. This is also true of the rich color, the adornments of the figure, and the background of pillows.

According to the legend, this portrait represents an aged, obese money-lender, whose unpleasant aroma attracts flying insects. Ironically, he is adorned with a bridegroom's crown — the symbol of youth and beauty. This devastating satire was presumably inspired by the indebtedness of the Rajput prince who commissioned the portrait.

BIBLIOGRAPHY: General reference: H. Goetz, *The Art and Architecture of Bikaner State*, 1950; B. Gray, *Treasures of Indian Miniatures in the Bikaner Palace Collection*, 1951; W. G. Archer, *Indian Painting from Rajasthan*, 1957.   *Lent by Mr. Stuart C. Welch, Jr.*

118.

WATER FESTIVAL AT UDAIPUR

India; Rajput (Mewar), mid-18th century (Jagat Singh II, 1734-1752).
Miniature painting; 18¼ x 23½″.

Although Rajput Mewar had staunchly resisted Mughal intrusions in the 16th century, the alliances of the 17th century brought increasing Mughal influence on the local, distinctly Rajput school of painting at Mewar. Further mingling of Rajput styles from Bundi and Kotah with those of Mewar may account for the Bundi and Kotah features of this work.

The painting shows a water festival at the Mewar capital of Udaipur. The bird's-eye view of the white pavilion, which served as a lake retreat for the Rajput nobility, conveys an illusion of depth that is characteristic of Mughal architectural drawing. The feeling of receding space in Mughal works has here been counteracted by the straight-on view of the hexagonal building at the right and the flat depiction of the lake as background for the figures. This reduction of spatial emphasis is typical of late Rajput painting. Mewar traits remain in the stylized detail of the trees and foliage, the established facial idioms, and the combination of geometric body structure with a refined flowing line. The rounded naturalistic forms of the water buffaloes are reminiscent of the dynamic incisive modeling and outline found in the Rajput painting of Bundi and Kotah. The clarity of line, sensitive use of color, and subtle grouping of figures and foliage within an architectural context lend a sense of accomplishment to this ambitious composition.

BIBLIOGRAPHY: General reference: M. Chandra, *Mewar Painting*, 1957; W. G. Archer, *Central Indian Painting*, 1958; _____, *Indian Painting in Bundi and Kotah*, 1959; S. C. Welch and M. C. Beach, *Gods, Thrones, and Peacocks* (catalogue of exhibition at Asia House), 1965.   *Lent by Mr. and Mrs. William P. Wood*

119.

DARBAR OF RAVAT JASWANT SINGH OF DEVGARH
India (Rajasthan); Devgarh, late 18th century.
Miniature painting; 15⅝ x 20 ⁵⁄₁₆″.

EXHIBITIONS: *Gods, Thrones, and Peacocks*, Asia House, New York, 1965-66, No. 62.

The *darbar*, or group portrait, owed its origin to Mughal sources. The people shown here were members of a rich and powerful nobility who ruled the principality of Devgarh in Mewar (Central India). These Rajput princes, noted for their bulk, were patrons of painting in the later 18th century.

Although Mughal influence on the art of the provinces — particularly those in Central India — waned with the weakening of the Mughal empire, it can still be seen in the realistic but lifeless faces which are delicately shaded on the cheeks. Features have a smooth unreal quality which is emphasized by harsh outlines. The background is reduced to a flat expanse that terminates in a cold horizon of narrow veridian foliage. A resurgence of local style is evident in the color and the agitated movement of the foreground, where drapery rhythms of the clothing lend brightness and vigor to an otherwise formal portrait. However, the apparent contradictions are not quite resolved. This work may be considered representative of the general decline in late 18th-century Rajput painting.

BIBLIOGRAPHY: Bearce and S. C. Welch, *Painting in British India, 1757-1857*, 1963, fig. 3.

Lent by Mr. Stuart C. Welch, Jr.

120.

HARE
Egypt; Fatimid, 12th century A.D.
Cast bronze; length 5⅞″.

The development of early Islamic art in Egypt was encouraged during the 200-year reign of the Moslem Fatimid dynasty. Despite the limited subject matter, as decreed in the Koran, the elaborate patterns devised by Islamic craftsmen often achieved a high level of artistry in the endless variation of simple motifs.

The heavy, somewhat awkward form of this cast bronze hare — with its disproportionately short legs and the summary treatment of its paws — is relieved by the expressive face and fanciful decoration. The entire surface of the figurine is patterned with complex designs framed by interlacing circles. This ornamental pattern may have been adapted from Coptic and Sasanian motifs by early Islamic artists who used them to vary an arabesque and calligraphic repertoire. The decoration may have been cut into the mold from which the hare was cast, but surface tooling was probably added to the finished product.

BIBLIOGRAPHY: G. Migeon, *Manuel d'art muselman*, 1927, I, fig. 187.

Lent by Mr. Stuart C. Welch, Jr.

121.

HEAD OF BUDDHA
Northwest Pakistan; Gandhara, 2nd century A.D.
Schist; height 8″.

EXHIBITIONS: *Hellenistic Art in Asia*, Fogg Art Museum, Cambridge, 1954, No. 40; *Evolution of the Buddha Image*, Asia House, New York, 1963, No. 1.

The head is typical of the Indo-Roman style of sculpture which flourished in the region of the Khyber Pass in the early centuries of our era. The intimate cultural and commercial relationships between the Kushan empire and the Roman West in this period led to an importation of a classical style and technique for the production of images and narrative reliefs used as decoration for the innumerable Buddhist establishments patronized by the royal house. It is probable that much of this carving was done with the collaboration of provincial workmen from Alexandria or the Roman East. In this head the soft effeminate features are derived from a Graeco-Roman Apollo type, and the wavy hair serves to disguise the *ushnisha*. Iconographical features, such as the elongated ear-lobes and *urna*, or mark between the brows, are Indian elements that have been combined with the Western technique.

Lent by Mr. Benjamin Rowland, Jr.

122.
GANÉSA
Central India; 9th century A.D.
Stone; height 20⅝"

This sculpture is a representation of one of the most beloved and widely worshiped Hindu deities — Ganésa, the elephant-faced god. Although several accounts of his creation exist, Ganésa is popularly accepted as the son of Siva and Parvati. As Ganapati he is the leader of the gnomelike Ganas, attendants of Siva, and in this aspect was worshiped by a mediveal sect (the Ganapatya) as their chief god. Also known as both the Lord and the Remover of Obstacles, Ganésa is invoked to remove various hindrances. Ganésa was one of the last divinities to be admitted to the Hindu pantheon; no traces of his cult can be found before the fifth century A.D., although it is believed that he is probably a survival of an earlier indigenous elephant god.

BIBLIOGRAPHY: S. Kramrisch, *Indian Sculpture*, 1933; A. Getty, *Ganésa: A Monograph on the Elephant-faced God*, 1936.

Lent by Mr. Stuart C. Welch, Jr.

123.
HEAD
Cambodia (Angkor complex); Khmer period, c.10th century A.D.
Stone; height 5".

Ultimately based upon Indian Gupta traditions, the sculptural style of the Khmers developed into one possessing both architectonic and sensuous qualities. Although small, this head displays many of the techniques used to combine these two seemingly opposed ends into a stylistic whole. When possible, everything is held close to the surface of the stone in order to preserve the image's overall cubic appearance. Only the most important facial features — the mouth with its upturned smile, the nose, and the eyebrows which almost seem applied rather than carved — break the surface. Other areas of the face are merely defined by incised lines (those of the upper lip and the eyes, for instance). The head bears a cylindrical coiffure of braided hair and an intricately carved diadem, whose prototype can be traced to a band encircling the lower portion of tall mitres frequently seen in earlier Cambodian scultpure.

BIBLIOGRAPHY: J. Boisselier, *La statuaire khmère et son évolution*, 1955.

Anonymous Loan

124.

LION

India; Mughal, c.1575.

Bronze; height 17⅜″.

While stone sculpture and small objects in stone and metal are familiar in Mughal art, this bronze, along with its now separated companion, is virtually unprecedented. When it first appeared on the international art market, it was described by some as European, by others as Chinese. A Mughal origin, however, is convincing on grounds of style and find spot. The combination of naturalism, as in the treatment of the leg muscles, and of extreme stylization, as in the mane, chests, ribs, and mask, is characteristic of early Mughal art. The surging rhythmic power of the stance and of the curves and counter-curves of the locks of hair in the mane invites comparison with Mughal art of the time when Akbar the Great (1557-1605) was building his empire. A strikingly similar lion was recorded and illustrated by a 17th-century traveler, Edward Terry, who was chaplain to Sir Thomas Roe, British ambassador to the Mughal court between 1615 and 1619. This regal beast, whose tail, body, and head — down to the curiously small ears, transformed in the sculpture into floral patterns — so resemble those of the lion shown here, is entitled by Terry "The Imperial Standard of the Great Mogol" (see William Foster, ed., *The Embassy of Sir Thomas Roe to the Court of the Great Mogol*, 1889, 11, pl. facing p. 322).

BIBLIOGRAPHY: Unpublished. General reference: S. C. Welch, *The Art of Mughal India*, 1963.

Lent by Mr. Stewart C. Welch, Jr.

125.

FRAGMENTARY SCULPTURE OF A BUDDHIST DEITY

Nepal; 17th century.

Gilt copper; height 17½″.

The figure portrayed is Vajradhara, one of the deities of the Vajrayana sect of Tantric Buddhism. Vajradhara, dressed in princely garments and ornaments, is the active agent of the Supreme Buddha. He is identified by the hands crossed against the chest, and though the attributes are missing, he would carry the *vajra*, or thunderbolt, in his right hand, and the *ghanta*, or bell, in his left.

The sculpture probably dates no earlier than the 17th century and demonstrates the limit to which an earlier style has been carried, still retaining a certain delicacy and grace. The pose is rather stiff, and there is a tendency toward abstraction of the natural forms which are given smooth rounded contours. The scarf and ornaments are symmetrically arranged and the roll of flesh over the belt exaggerated. Yet the face is individually modeled and the expression sweet and youthful. The eyebrows and eyes are delicately outlined, echoing the graceful delineation of the fingers. The feeling of softness of the flesh is retained and contrasts with the sharp and precise details of jewelry inlaid with semiprecious stones.

BIBLIOGRAPHY: A. Getty, *The Gods of Northern Buddhism*, 1928; S. Kramrisch, *The Art of Nepal*, 1964.

Lent by Mr. and Mrs. James Biddle

126.

SEATED FIGURE

Western China (found in the Lung-men caves); No. Wei dynasty (318-535 A.D.).

Gray limestone; height 26½″.

In 493, the capital of the No. Wei dynasty was moved from Ta-t'ung in Shansi province to Loyang, located 500 miles south in Honan province, the heartland of Chinese territory. South of the new capital, along the western bank of the Yi River, a series of Buddhist cave-temples were excavated from the limestone cliff. The site was named Lung-men, or Dragon Gate, and work was begun soon after the transfer of the capital. Several important caves, excavated on imperial order, were completed by the first quarter of the 6th century and represent the high point of No. Wei accomplishments in religious sculpture. These cave-temples are generally rectangular in plan with a vaulted ceiling. The main Buddha image, flanked by attendants, was carved from the rear wall.

This sculpture is probably from a secondary wall niche. The figure is identified as Maitreya, the Buddha of the Future. He is shown seated in a meditative pose with crossed ankles in Central Asian fashion. The repetitive elaboration of the folds of drapery is a typical feature of the Lung-men style of the 6th century.

BIBLIOGRAPHY: A. Priest, *Chinese Sculpture in The Metropolitan Museum of Art*, 1944; L. Sickman and A. Soper, *The Art and Architecture of China*, 1956.   *Lent by Mr. and Mrs. James Biddle*

127.
DAINICHI NYORAI
Japan; Late Heian period, mid-11th century.
Hinoli wood, single block construction, slight traces of original color and gilt lacquer; height with base 24½″.

The Shingon sect of Tantric Buddhism was introduced to Japan by the priest Kukai who returned from China in 807 A.D. This sculpture represents Dainichi Nyorai, the Supreme Buddha of this esoteric sect. He is shown seated in a meditative attitude with legs crossed, the right foot over and in front of the left, the soles of both feet turned upward. Dainichi Nyorai is dressed in the garb and ornaments of a Bodhisattva, a being in the Buddhist pantheon who has attained enlightenment but remains on earth to teach the Way. The hands are held in a special gesture, or *mudra*: the index finger of the left hand is clasped by the five fingers of the right to symbolize the mystic union — achieved through meditation — of the individual consciousness and the Universal Spirit. On the crown are engraved small Buddha figures, each placed at one of the Four Directions; they are considered emanations of the Supreme and central Buddha.

This sect remained popular into the Late Heian period (894-1185), and the style of this sculpture would indicate a date in the mid-11th century. The somber and threatening bearing of 9th-century Buddhist sculpture has given way to a benevolent and mild expression. The eyes are downcast and a slight smile plays on the lips. The full round forms of the body are simplified, and the drapery is arranged in a few parallel folds, delicately carved.

BIBLIOGRAPHY: A. Getty, *The Gods of Northern Buddhism*, 1928; T. Kuno, *A Guide to Japanese Sculpture*, 1963.   *Lent by Mr. Henry F. Harrison*

128.
ZOCHO TEN, GUARDIAN OF THE SOUTH
Japan; Late Heian period (897-1185).
Bronze; height 7¾″.

The four guardian figures included in the Mahayana Buddhist pantheon originated in Hindu mythology as beings who dwelt on Mount Sumeru and guarded the Four Cardinal Points of the world. From India, Mahayana Buddhism spread through Central Asia into China. By the 6th century, Buddhism had been introduced to Japan, where the four guardians, known as the Shitenno or Four Heavenly Kings, became popular along with the principal deities of the sect. The four guardians were usually placed on the four corners of the altar platform, as symbolic protectors of the faith. Many fine examples of the Shitenno date from the 7th and 8th centuries and also from the Late Heian period when Mahayana beliefs regained popularity after a period of decline. The Heian figures show that earlier attempts to indicate a dynamic stance and naturalistic drapery had been achieved.

Zocho Ten is represented as a warrior wearing plate armor and undergarments characteristic of the Chinese style of the 7th century. He is identified by the raised right arm which once held a drawn sword or lance. He is often shown trampling demons underfoot. The figure is well proportioned and heavy-set. The sleeve and skirt are naturally rendered, giving a sense of freedom for movement. The facial features are summarily treated; the threatening expression is convincing but not terrifying. The traditional conception of the four guardians as dignified and calm beings has added an element of restraint in the execution of this figure.

BIBLIOGRAPHY: A. Getty, *The Gods of Northern Buddhism*, 1928; T. Kuno, *A Guide to Japanese Sculpture*, 1963.

Lent by Mr. and Mrs. James Biddle

129.
ACOLYTE OF THE KASUGA SHRINE
Japan; Kamakura period (1185-1333).
Wood; height 20″.

The figure represented is an acolyte of the Kasuga Shrine, a Shinto shrine built by the Fujiwara family at Nara as a sanctuary for their ancestral deities. Originally the native Shinto religion had no icons. The representation of Shinto deities was motivated by the belief, popular during the Kamakura period, that Shinto deities were manifestations of the Buddhist gods. Shrines were built within the compounds of Buddhist monasteries as seats for the protecting Shinto gods, and the style of Shinto sculpture was determined by the artists and workshops already producing Buddhist icons.

The forms of both the figure and the drapery of this sculpture are boldly simplified; only a few deep folds delineate the volume of the sash and skirt. The rough chisel marks have been deliberately left as an indication of the artist's respect for his material and for the tradition of craftsmanship.

BIBLIOGRAPHY: A. Getty, *The Gods of Northern Buddhism*, 1928; T. Kuno, *A Guide to Japanese Sculpture*, 1963; H. Munsterberg, *Mingei: Folk Arts of Old Japan*, 1965, pl. 60.

Lent by Mr. Henry F. Harrison

130.
RITUAL VESSEL
China; Late Shang dynasty (1300-1027 B.C.).
Bronze; height 10¾″.

This bronze vessel is identified in Chinese literature as a *chueh*, a wine goblet used in ritual ceremonies when offerings of food and drink were made to ancestors. This vessel type is characterized by the troughlike spout, three tapering legs, and pair of upright capped posts.

The tall graceful shape with rounded bottom is similar to examples known to have been excavated from Anyang, site of the last capital of the Shang dynasty. This shape is typical of the late phase of development of the type, which was not continued into the succeeding Chou dynasty. Characteristic of Late Shang bronze decoration, the major designs are in relief against a background of engraved spirals. The profile of the vessel is emphasized by a bold segmented flange which divides the decoration into sections. The upper portion is ornamented with rising blades which vary in height according to the flare of the mouth. On the lower portion, the principal motif is the *t'ao-t'ieh*, or animal mask, identified by the raised eye on either side of the flange, the horn above the eye, the ear to the side, and the portion of the upper jaw below. A vertical dragon appears as a space filler. The delicate and refined decoration is covered with small spirals to harmonize with the background and is appropriately scaled to suit the size and shape of the vessel.

Lent by Mr. Stuart C. Welch, Jr.

131.
THREE ANIMAL MASKS: (a) OWL'S HEAD and (b) TWO FANTASTIC ANIMALS*
China; Chou dynasty (1027-256 B.C.).
Bronze; (a) width 2¹¹⁄₁₆″ and (b) height 7¹⁄₁₆″ each.

The mask in the shape of an owl's head reveals the artist's ability to transform the characteristic features of the bird into a simple, almost abstract, geometric design. In the same way, the particular features of the fantastic animal heads are greatly simplified. The repeated shapes are emphasized by the bold contours and precise edges and create a rhythmic symmetrical design. The owl's head may have been used on horse trappings placed over the forehead of the animal, and the fantastic animal heads on chariots as decorative elements.

Lent by Mr. Stuart C. Welch, Jr.

* Only one is illustrated.

132.
HORSE
China; T'ang dynasty (618-907, A.D.).
Glazed pottery, maximum height 17″, maximum length 21″.

EXHIBITIONS: Lyman Allen Museum, New London, Conn.

The Chinese, in a practice similar to the burial customs of other cultures, equipped the funerary chamber with pottery replicas of persons and objects with which the deceased was familiar during his life and would need for life beyond the grave. Some of these objects, known as *ming-ch'i*, were substitutes for the living beings that had once been sacrificed for the burial. The profusion of burial objects found in tombs has provided us with an almost complete picture of everyday life at various periods of Chinese history.

During the T'ang dynasty great variety appears within the types of figurines. The different classes of society were carefully ranked, and sumptuary laws regulated the size and number of figurines allowed to each rank. Usually a pair or more of horses was placed in the tomb, along with figures of richly attired court ladies, court and military officials, ensembles of musicians and dancing girls, camel drivers with their loaded pack animals, and merchants from various regions who came from the West across Central Asia to sell their exotic wares in the bustling and prosperous cities.

The horse displayed is a fine example of T'ang workmanship of the late 7th-8th century. Its saddle and trappings were modeled separately and applied before firing. The buff-colored body is covered by a white slip over which the glazes were applied and fired at medium temperature. The monochrome lead glazes typical of T'ang ceramic decoration are thinly applied and allowed to run, producing the characteristic mottled effect.

BIBLIOGRAPHY: J. G. Mahler, *The Westerners Among the Figurines of the T'ang Dynasty of China*, 1959.

Lent by Mr. and Mrs. James Biddle

133.

CELESTIAL DANCER

China; Sung dynasty, 12th-13th century.
Sun-baked clay; height 13 5/8".

This charming figure wears a long-sleeved tunic and skirt; its jeweled crown with ribbons and the necklace are summarily modeled. The body is shown poised and balanced in a lively dance posture, the torso bent at the waist, the head turned, and the right leg advanced. The long sleeves held in position by the arms and the billowing scarves enhance the feeling of motion. The exaggerated fluttering and curling of the scarves is also characteristic of certain Buddhist iconographic drawings and figure paintings in this period. The clay was probably reinforced with wire in order to model the scarves and sleeves. This figure may have been part of a group depicting a Paradise Scene.

Lent by Mr. and Mrs. James Biddle

134.

JAR

Japan; Jomon period, 3rd millenium B.C.
Terracotta; height 12 1/4".

The clay vessels and figurines of the Jomon period are among the earliest artistic works of Japan. Carbon-14 sampling techniques have been used to date the period as early as 7000 B.C. The period, which continues to 200 B.C. and corresponds to the Neolithic era, is divided into several styles and techniques.

The wheel was unknown to the Jomon potter who used coils of clay to build up the required shape, then baked the vessels in open fires at a low temperature. Roughly translated Jomon means "cord pattern," a name describing the manner of decoration. Ropelike fibers were pressed into the unfired clay, either in single strands or after being wound around a large stick in order to decorate a large area quickly. Sharp-edged shells and pointed bamboo sticks were also used to incise decoration, as were sticks carved with patterns which were rolled on the surface.

This tall vase, with its flattened base and slightly shaped sides, is characteristic of the later Jomon period. The creative imagination of the potter and his feeling for the clay as a highly plastic substance are clearly evident in the way the rim and sculptured handle have been built up by molding the clay mass and adding thin clay strips. Curved or straight lines gauged into the surface to decorate the rim contrast with the more refined decoration of the lower portion. The contrasts of heavy mass, bold relief, cut-out areas, and patterns of varying textures reveal a sophisticated potter striving for a very conscious effect well within his range of technical skill.

BIBLIOGRAPHY: General reference: F. Koyama, *Japanese Ceramics from Ancient to Modern Times*, 1961; P. C. Swann, *The Art of Japan from the Jomon to the Tokugawa Period*, 1966.

Lent by Mr. Stuart C. Welch, Jr.

135.

PORCELAIN JAR

Japan; Edo period, last quarter of the 17th century.
Kakiemon ware, with decoration of herons and willows in underglaze blue; height 15″.

Porcelain was first produced in Japan at the beginning of the Edo period (1615-1868). This was a surprisingly late development, since porcelain had been perfected in China by the 8th century A.D. In 1616 a Korean potter who had immigrated to Japan discovered on the southern island of Kyushu a fine quality clay suitable for porcelain. The first true porcelain-ware kiln was established on Kyushu, and the early pieces were decorated in an underglaze design in cobalt blue. By the mid-17th century potters of the Kakiemon family, working near the village of Arita, had perfected the technique of decoration in overglaze colors added before a second firing. Inspiration for this type of decoration came from imported porcelain of the Ming and Ch'ing dynasties of China.

In keeping with the early phase of porcelain decoration, only underglaze blue has been used to render the bold pictorial designs of herons resting in trees. The gray-white ground effectively suggests an expanse of water and sky with decorative cloud forms. The placing of the branches utilizes the broad contour of the jar to suggest the curve of the branch in space, with resting herons and leaves hanging down on each side.

BIBLIOGRAPHY: General reference: R. A. Miller, *Japanese Ceramics*, 1960; F. Koyama,
Japanese Ceramics From Ancient to Modern Times, 1961.   *Lent by Mr. Henry F. Harrison*

136.

PIED WAGTAIL ON A LOTUS FROND

China; Yüan dynasty (1279-1368).
Color on silk; 11¼ x 16″.

EXHIBITIONS: *Masterpieces of Chinese Bird and Flower Painting*, Fogg Art Museum, Cambridge, 1951, No. 20.

This painting may have been cut from a longer scroll. In its softly fused, pastel-like wash technique, it is typical of the delicate textural realism initiated by the famous master, Ch'ien Hsüan (1235-90). The picture is a typical Yüan survival of the kind of "magic realism" developed by the Emperor Hui Tsung and his academy in the 12th century for the representation of birds and flowers, often as poetic emblems of seasonal change.

A seal of Hsiang Mo-lin (1525-90) appears in the lower right hand corner.

BIBLIOGRAPHY: T. Bowie, *East-West in Art*, 1966, p. 42, fig. 36.   *Lent by Mr. Benjamin Rowland, Jr.*

137.

SEISHI BOSATSU

Japan; Late Heian period (897-1185).
Color on silk; 39⅝ x 22¼″.

This is a representation of a Bodhisattva (Japanese, Bosatsu), a divine being — the Buddhist equivalent of an archangel — who descends as an emissary from the Paradise of the immortal Buddha to the world of men. The painting was part of a triptych with the portrayal of Amida, the Buddha of Light, in the central panel, and a banner of Kannon, the Lord of Compassion, at the left. It is an isolated replica of the same figure in the famous triptych at Koyasan, attributed to the 11th-century priest Eishin Sozu, who had a mystic vision of Amida and his heavenly retinue in the skies above Lake Biwa. Although some scholars have suggested that this picture might be a copy of the Kamakura period, the refinement of the wiry drawing and the persistence of the abstract shading technique of earlier periods of Japanese painting strongly suggest that this *kakemono* is a nearly contemporary replica of the Koyasan version. The painting is an embodiment of the aristocratic refinement and feminine ideal of Buddhist art in the chivalric age of *The Tale of Genji*.

BIBLIOGRAPHY: B. Rowland, Jr., *Art in East and West*, 1954 and 1966, pl. 24; T. Bowie, *East-West in Art*, 1966, p. 31, fig. 18; J. Mayuyama, *Japanese Art in the West*, 1966, No. 87, p. 75.   *Lent by Mr. Benjamin Rowland, Jr.*

138.

FLOWERS IN MOONLIGHT

SAKAI HOITSU (Japanese), 1761-1828.
Hanging scroll, colors on silk; 56½ x 19⅝".

Some of the most beautiful and striking works of the Edo period were painted by the two masters Sotatsu (1576-1643) and Korin (1658-1716). Sotatsu's highly original and personal style, though based in part on earlier traditions, displayed a bold stylization of natural forms, with colors juxtaposed to create a consciously decorative composition. Korin continued this decorative style which, however, was not perpetuated by any school of artists. Sakai Hoitsu later in the century revived his earlier style and stimulated appreciation for the work of Korin. Born into a noble family, Hoitsu spent most of his life in such artistic pursuits as painting, poetry, and calligraphy. His oeuvre shows many styles but most obviously those of Sotatsu and Korin. This painting, however, lacks the careful and balanced composition of those earlier masters but reveals Hoitsu's elegant taste and refinement.

BIBLIOGRAPHY: R. T. Paine and A. C. Soper, *The Art and Architecture of Japan*, 1955; T. Akiyama, *Japanese Painting*, 1961.   *Lent by Mr. Henry F. Harrison*

139.

WOMAN UNDER SNOWY WILLOW

KITAO MASANOBU (Japanese), 1761-1816.
Hanging scroll, ink and colors on paper; 49¾ x 18¼".

Kitao Masanobu was a leading artist in the color wood-block print technique. But early in his precocious career (about 1789), he turned to writing novels and comic poems, for which he is also well known. This hanging scroll painting is signed Santo Kyoden, the pseudonym he used as a writer, and must therefore date after 1789. In the upper right hand corner of the scroll one of his poems is inscribed. Masanobu has chosen a traditional subject of the color print, using brush with ink and color rather than the multiple wood-block technique. The snowscape and willow are delineated with a minimum of detail, and the graceful figure is silhouetted against the white expanse, further enhancing the outline of the form. With a few bold brushstrokes, which are varied by the tonality of the ink and by the thickness of application, the artist has been able to suggest the volume of the figure beneath the kimono. The mood of the painting is consciously poetic and introduces us to an aspect of the artist's personality which is quite different from his more traditional color wood-block prints.

BIBLIOGRAPHY: General reference: M. Gentles, *Masters of the Japanese Print*, 1964; J. Hillier, *Japanese Color Prints*, 1964; M. W. Young and R. J. Smith, *Oriental Art*, XIII, No. 2 (1967).   *Lent by Mr. Henry F. Harrison*

Plates

25. Conde Don Francisco Diaz de la Reguera. *Perseus and Andromeda.*
Second half of 16th century. Lent by **Mr. Benjamin Rowland, Jr.**

36. Paul Serusier. *The Farmhouse at Le Pouldu.* 1890. Lent by Mr. Alexander M. Laughlin.

42. Joseph M. W. Turner. *Mainz and Kastell.* 1817. Lent by Mr. and Mrs. James Biddle.

67. Albert Bierstadt.
California Redwoods. c. 1870.
Lent by Mr. John C. Wilmerding, Jr.

87. Henri Matisse. *Girl with a Hat*. 1920. Lent by Mr. Lee A. Ault.

102b. *Hushang Slays the Black Div*. Folio from the *Shahnama* manuscript. 1520-40.
Lent by Mr. Arthur A. Houghton, Jr.

Primitive Art

1. *"Bird Stone."* American Indian,
date unknown. Anonymous loan.

2. *Head of a dignitary.*
Remojades culture, c.200-600 A.D.
Lent by Mr. and Mrs. Dixon Stanton.

3. *Finial in the form of a bird.* Pre-Columbian,
8th-10th century A.D.
Collection George Ortiz, Geneva.

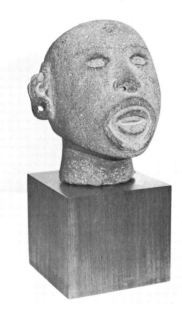

5. *Seated figure.* Baole tribe,
c.15th century A.D.
Lent by Mr. Lee A. Ault.

4. *Head of a man with mask.*
Toltec, c.10th-12th century A.D.
Lent by Mr. Lee A. Ault.

6. *Head.* "South Niger," c.17th century A.D.
Collection George Ortiz, Geneva.

7. *Reliquary head.* Bakota tribe,
19th century A.D.
Lent by Mr. Paul M. Ingersoll.

Ancient Art

8. *Seated monkey*. Proto-Elamite,
early 3rd millennium B.C.
Lent by Mr. Stuart C. Welch, Jr.

9. *Mare on solid base*. Greek,
8th century B.C.
Collection George Ortiz, Geneva.

10. *Fibula.* Lydian or Phrygian, 8th-7th century B.C.
Lent by Mr. Stuart C. Welch, Jr.

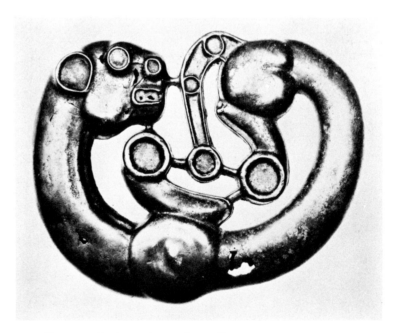

11. *Plaque in the form of a panther or lioness.*
Scythian, 7th-6th century B.C.
Lent by Mr. Stuart C. Welch, Jr.

12. *Youth in helmet and boots.*
Greek, c.520 B.C.
Collection George Ortiz, Geneva.

13. *Standing diskophoros.* Graeco-Roman
copy of a classical original. Lent by Mr. Benjamin Rowland, Jr.
(Courtesy, Museum of Fine Arts, Boston).

14. *Plate with relief medallion* (detail).
Greek c.360 B.C.
Collection George Ortiz, Geneva.

15. *Female head*. Greek, 4th century B.C.
Anonymous loan.

16. *Ibis*. Ptolemaic, c.300 B.C.
Anonymous loan.

17. *Plate with the "goddess Anahita."*
Sasanian 5th-6th century A.D.
Lent by Mr. Stuart C. Welch, Jr.

European Art

18. *Elizabethan tankard.* 1602.
Lent by Mr. Arthur A. Houghton, Jr.

19. Danese Cattaneo. *Ceres.*
Second half of 16th century.
Anonymous loan.

20. Anonymous Italian. *Vulcan*. 16th century.
Anonymous loan.

21. Francesco Susini. *Crouching Aphrodite*.
17th century. Anonymous loan.

22. *The Eucharist.* Russian icon, 16th century.
Lent by Mr. Stuart C. Welch, Jr.

23. "Vicino da Ferrara." *St. George.* c.1480.
Lent by Mr. and Mrs. James Biddle.

24. Giovanni Stradanus. *Rearing Horse.*
Late 16th-early 17th century. Lent by Mr. Benjamin Rowland, Jr.

26. Lucas Cranach. *Princess Sibylle of Cleves.* c.1525.
Lent by Mr. Arthur A. Houghton, Jr.

27. Joos van Cleve. *Portrait of Francis I.* c.1530.
Lent by Mr. Arthur A. Houghton, Jr.

28. Marten van Heemskerck. *The Horse-tamers of Montecavallo.* 16th century.
Lent by Mr. Benjamin Rowland, Jr.

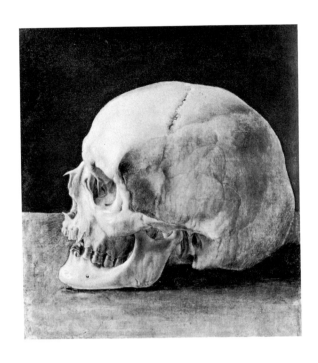

29. Hercules Seghers. *Skull.*
First half of 17th century.
Anonymous loan.

30. The Flora Master.
Profile head of a Woman (Procris?).
c.1540-60. Lent by Mr. Benjamin Rowland, Jr.

31. Jean-Honoré Fragonard. Two drawings for *Orlando Furioso*. 1780s.
Lent by Mr. Arthur A. Houghton, Jr.

32. Eugène Delacroix. *Arab Horseman on Patrol.* 1851.
Anonymous loan.

33. Honoré Daumier. *Leaving the Theater.* After 1848.
Lent by Mr. Charles W. Engelhard.

34. Gustave Courbet. *Hunters in the Snow*. 1866.
Lent by Mr. Charles W. Engelhard.

35. Mary Cassatt. *The Nurse*.
Second half of 19th century.
Lent by Mr. A. Varick Stout.

37. Richard Wilson. *Classical Landscape.* c.1751-58 (?).
Lent by Professor and Mrs. E. Dudley H. Johnson.

38. John Constable. *Near Dedham.*
Lent by Mr. and Mrs. James Biddle.

39. William Etty. *Four Studies of Aeneas Fleeing the Burning Troy*.
First half of 19th century. Lent by Mr. Frederick B. Adams.

40. John Robert Cozens. *The Lake of Nemi*. 1789.
Lent by Mr. and Mrs. James Biddle.

41. William Blake. *The Death of St. Joseph*. c.1803.
Lent by Mr. and Mrs. James Biddle.

43. John Sell Cotman. *Landscape with a Ruined Abbey*. First half of 19th century.
Lent by Professor and Mrs. E. Dudley H. Johnson.

44. William Henry Hunt. *Ferns, Grass, and Flowers.*
19th century. Lent by Mr. and Mrs. James Biddle.

45. William Purser. *Shipping Off Shore with Approaching Storm.*
First half of 19th century.
Lent by Mr. and Mrs. James Biddle.

46. Sir Edwin Henry Landseer. *A Falconer*. 1837.
Lent by Professor and Mrs. E. Dudley H. Johnson.

47. Edward Lear. *Study of Trees*. 1839.
Lent by Mr. and Mrs. James Biddle.

48. Joseph M. W. Turner. *The Splügen Pass.* 1842.
Lent by Mr. and Mrs. James Biddle.

49. David Cox. *Haymaking in Wales.* 1850.
Lent by Professor and Mrs. E. Dudley H. Johnson.

50. Samuel Palmer.
*The Waterfall at Pistil Mawddach,
Near Dolgelly, N. Wales.* 1835(?)
Lent by Mr. and Mrs. James Biddle.

American Art

51. Henricus Boelen. *Wine Taster*. 18th century.
Lent by Mr. Gardner D. Stout.

52. Adrian Bancker. *Tankard*. c.1678.
Lent by Mr. Gardner D. Stout.

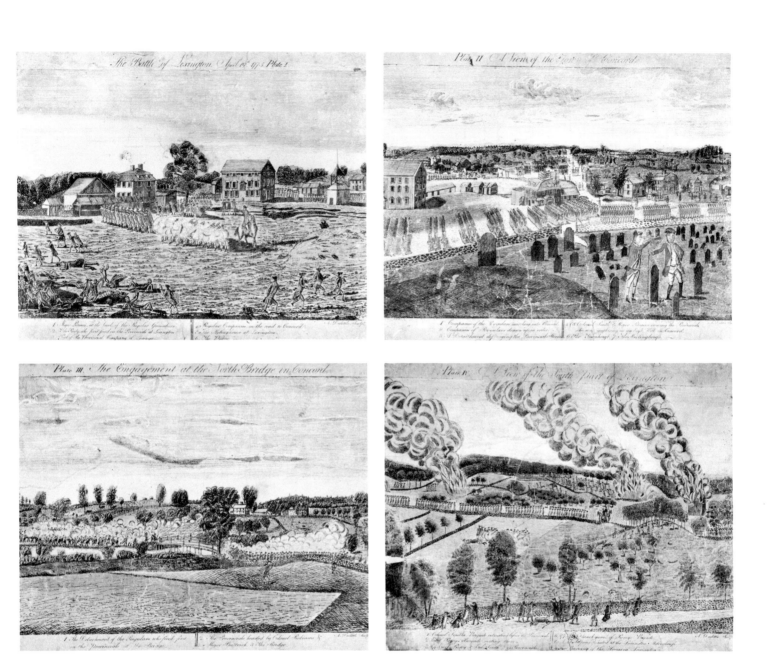

53. Amos Doolittle. *Views of the Battles of Lexington and Concord.*
Lent by Mr. Harry W. Havemeyer.

54. John Neagle. *Red Jacket*. 1824.
Lent by Mr. Benjamin R. Neilson.

55. Thomas Cole. *Mill Dam on the Catskill Creek*. 1841.
Lent by Mr. Henry M. Fuller.

56. Thomas Sully. *Portrait of Moncure Robinson.* 1849.
Lent by Mr. Alexander O. Vietor.

57. Fitz Hugh Lane. *Stage Rocks and Western Shore of Gloucester Outer Harbor.* c.1852.
Lent by Mr. John C. Wilmerding, Jr.

58. George Caleb Bingham. *Mississippi Flatboatman*. 1850.
Lent by Mr. John C. Wilmerding, Jr.

60. Frederick Edwin Church. *Sunrise in the Cordilleras.* 1854.
Lent by Mr. John C. Wilmerding, Jr.

61. Arthur Fitzwilliam Tait.
Woodduck, Green-winged Teal, and Bufflehead. 1863.
Lent by Mr. and Mrs. Pieter W. Fosburgh, Cherry Plain.

62. Eastman Johnson. *Woman Polishing Glasses*. 1863.
Lent by Mr. Henry M. Fuller.

63. Martin Johnson Heade. *Twilight in the Salt Marshes.* c.1863-65.
Lent by Mr. John C. Wilmerding, Jr.

64. Martin Johnson Heade. *Lake Atitlán, Guatemala.* 1867.
Lent by Mr. John C. Wilmerding, Jr.

65. Robert S. Dunning. *Still Life: Red Cherries.* 1866.
Lent by Mr. Henry M. Fuller.

66. Jasper Cropsey. *The Eagle's Nest.* 1867.
Lent by Mr. and Mrs. Pieter W. Fosburgh, Cherry Plain.

68. John Linton Chapman. *The Appian Way*. 1879.
Lent by Mr. Henry M. Fuller.

69. Winslow Homer. *Through the Fields*. 1879.
Lent by Mr. Charles W. Engelhard.

70. Winslow Homer. *Hunter and Dog, Adirondacks*. 1889.
Lent by Mr. and Mrs. Pieter W. Fosburgh, Cherry Plain.

71. Winslow Homer. *Deer Drinking*. 1892.
Lent by Mr. Cortlandt P. Dixon.

72. John Frederick Peto. *Still Life with Pottery Mug, Newspaper, Pipe, Matches, and Oyster Cracker.*
Second half of 19th century.
Lent by Mr. Frank T. Howard.

73. Joseph Decker. *Twenty-three Pears.*
Lent by Mr. Stuart C. Welch, Jr.

Twentieth-Century Western Art

74. Aristide Maillol.
Pomona with Lowered Arms.
Lent by Mr. R. Sturgis Ingersoll.

75. Jacques Lipchitz. *Rape of Europa.* 1940s.
Lent by Mr. R. Sturgis Ingersoll.

76. Alexander Calder. *The Encounter*. 1956.
Lent by Mr. Lee A. Ault.

77. Gerhard Marcks.
Standing Girl with Hand on Head. 1960.
Lent by Mr. Paul M. Ingersoll.

130

78. Edgar Negret. *La Columna*. 1964.
Lent by Mr. Lee A. Ault, III.

79. Pablo Picasso. *Au Café*. 1902.
Lent by Mr. Lee A. Ault.

131

80. Pablo Picasso. *Head of a Boy*. 1906.
Lent by Mr. Lee A. Ault.

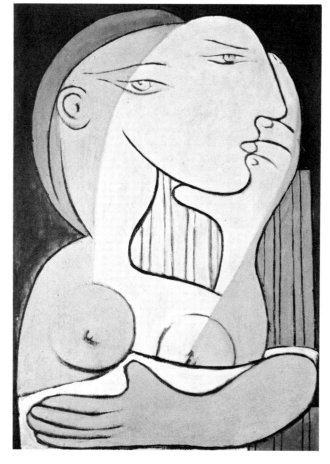

81. Pablo Picasso. *Seated Woman*. 1932.
Lent by Mr. Lee A. Ault.

82. Pablo Picasso. *Owl.* 1950.
Lent by Mr. Lee A. Ault.

83. Pablo Picasso. *Plate with faun and owl.* 1957.
Lent by Mr. Lee A. Ault.

84. Edouard Vuillard. *Woman Reading.*
Lent by Mr. Lee A. Ault.

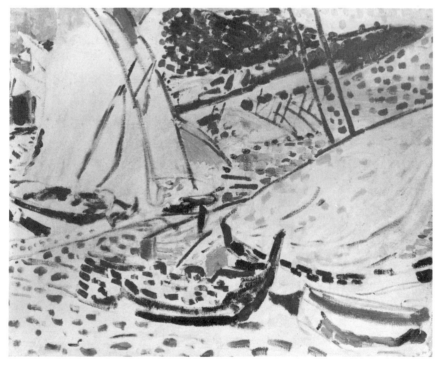

85. André Derain. *Sailboats at Collioure.* 1905.
Lent by Mr. Charles W. Engelhard.

86. Georges Rouault. *Nude Standing.* 1905
Lent by Mr. Lee A. Ault.

88. Roger de la Fresnaye. *Self-Portrait.* 1920.
Lent by Professor and Mrs. E. Dudley H. Johnson.

89. Georges Braque. *Woman with Mandolin*. 1931.
Lent by Mr. Lee A. Ault.

90. Yves Tanguy. *La Lumière de l'ombre*. 1939.
Lent by Mr. Hugh J. Chisolm, Jr.

91. Paul Klee. *The Gatekeeper's Pride*. 1929.
Lent by Mr. Lee A. Ault.

92. Marc Chagall. *Grand Nu Jaune*. 1949.
Lent by Mr. Hugo V. Neuhaus, Jr.

93. George Luks. *West Side Docks*. 1905.
Lent by Mr. Roderick H. Cushman.

94. Maurice B. Prendergast. *Early Evening*. c.1917-20
Lent by Mr. Roderick H. Cushman.

95. Charles Demuth. *New England Houses.* 1918.
Lent by Mr. Benjamin Rowland, Jr.

96. John Marin. *Maples in Autumn Foliage.* 1949.
Lent by Mr. and Mrs. William P. Wood.

97. Mark Rothko. *Abstract Painting, Untitled*. 1951.
Anonymous loan.

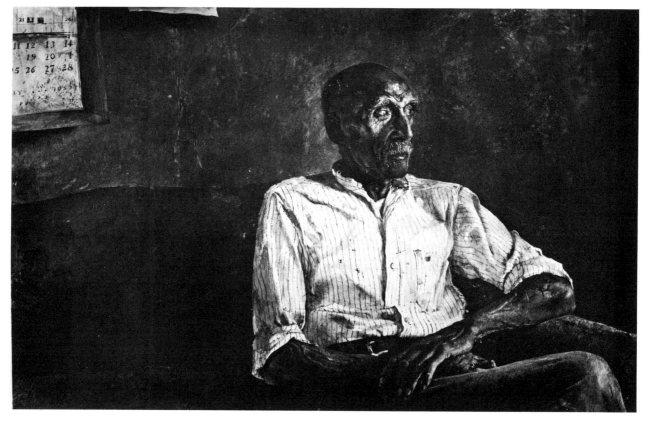

98. Andrew Wyeth. *Citizen Clark*. 1957. Lent by Mr. Alexander M. Laughlin.

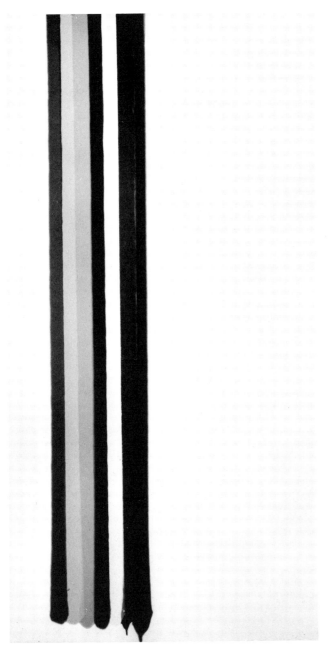

99. Morris Louis. *Untitled: Stripe Series*. 1961.
Anonymous loan.

100. Walter Murch. *Bread and Cloth*. 1965.
Lent by Mr. Lee A. Ault.

Oriental Art

101. *Bizhan Ridding the Land of the Wild Boar.*
Persian miniature, 14th century.
Lent by Mr. Stuart C. Welch, Jr.

102a. *Rosette.*
Folio from the *Shahnama* manuscript, 1520-40.
Lent by Mr. Arthur A. Houghton, Jr.

102c. *The Death of Zahhak.*
Folio from the *Shahnama* manuscript, 1520-40.
Lent by Mr. Arthur A. Houghton, Jr.

102d. *Zal is Sighted by a Caravan.*
Folio from the *Shahnama* manuscript, 1520-40.
Lent by Mr. Arthur A. Houghton, Jr.

102e. *Zal Entertains Mihrab at Kabul.*
Folio from the *Shahnama* manuscript, 1520-40.
Lent by Mr. Arthur A. Houghton, Jr.

102f. *Rustam Before Kay Qubad.*
Folio from the *Shahnama* manuscript, 1520-40.
Lent by Mr. Arthur A. Houghton, Jr.

103. *Gabriel Announcing the Apotheosis of 'Ali.*
Persian miniature, c.1450-77.
Lent by Mr. Stuart C. Welch, Jr.

104. *The Celebration of 'Id.*
Persian miniature, 16th century.
Lent by Mr. Stuart C. Welch, Jr.

105. *Youth with a Wine Cup.*
Persian miniature, c.1560-70.
Lent by Mr. Stuart C. Welch, Jr.

106. *Man and Monkey Riding a Nag.*
Persian miniature, c.1590.
Lent by Mr. Stuart C. Welch, Jr.

107. *Album Page.*
Persian calligraphy, 16th century.
Lent by Mr. Stuart C. Welch, Jr.

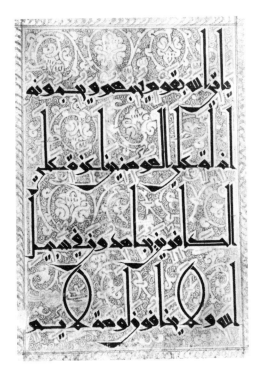

108. *Folio from a Koran.*
Seljuk calligraphy, 12th century.
Lent by Mr. Stuart C. Welch, Jr.

109. *Dragon.* Turkish or Persian drawing, c.1560.
Lent by Mr. Stuart C. Welch, Jr.

110. *Battle Scene* from a *Bhagavata Purana* series. Indian miniature, c.1540 or earlier.
Lent by Mr. Stuart C. Welch, Jr.

111. *Kurshidchehr Frees Hamid* from the *Dastan i Amir Hamza*. Indian miniature, c.1570 .
Lent by Mr. Stuart C. Welch, Jr.

112. *A Dervish and a Musician.*
Indian miniature, c.1609.
Lent by Mr. Stuart C. Welch, Jr.

113. *Rama and Lakshman Converse with an Ascetic.* Indian miniature, c.1635.
Lent by Mr. Stuart C. Welch, Jr.

114. *Ram Singh of Kotah Pursuing a Rhinoceros*. Indian miniature, c.1700.
Lent by Mr. Stuart C. Welch, Jr.

115. *Krishna Fluting in a Wood*.
Indian miniature, early 18th century.
Lent by Mr. Stuart C. Welch, Jr.

116. *The Month of Magha* from a *Baramasa* set.
Indian miniature, c.1720.
Lent by Mr. Stuart C. Welch, Jr.

117. *Portrait of Trilokha Khatri as a Bridegroom.*
Indian miniature, c.1725.
Lent by Mr. Stuart C. Welch, Jr.

118. *Water Festival at Udaipur*. Indian miniature, mid-18th century.
Lent by Mr. and Mrs. William P. Wood.

119. *Darbar of Ravat Jaswant Singh of Devgarh*. Indian miniature, late 18th century.
Lent by Mr. Stuart C. Welch, Jr.

120. *Hare.* Fatimid, 12th century. Lent by Mr. Stuart C. Welch, Jr.

121. *Head of Buddha.*
Gandharan, 2nd century A.D.
Lent by Mr. Benjamin Rowland, Jr.
(Courtesy, Fogg Art Museum, Harvard University,
Cambridge, Massachusetts).

122. *Ganeśa*. Central Indian, 9th century A.D.
Lent by Mr. Stuart C. Welch, Jr.

123. *Head*. Cambodian, Khmer period, c.10th century.
Anonymous loan.

124. *Lion*. Indian, Mughal, c.1575.
Lent by Mr. Stuart C. Welch, Jr.

125. *Fragmentary sculpture of a
Buddhist deity*.Nepalese, 17th century.
Lent by Mr. and Mrs. James Biddle.

126. *Seated figure.* Chinese, No. Wei dynasty.
Lent by Mr. and Mrs. James Biddle.

127. *Dainichi Nyorai.*
Japanese, Late Heian period,
mid-11th century. Lent by Mr. Henry F. Harrison.

128. *Zocho Ten, Guardian of the South.*
Japanese, Late Heian period.
Lent by Mr. and Mrs. James Biddle.

129. *Acolyte of the Kasuga Shrine.*
Japanese, Kamakura period.
Lent by Mr. Henry F. Harrison.

130. *Ritual vessel.*
Chinese, late Shang dynasty.
Lent by Mr. Stuart C. Welch, Jr.

131. *Animal masks:* (a) *owl;* (b) *fantastic animal.*
Chinese, Chou dynasty.
Lent by Mr. Stuart C. Welch, Jr.

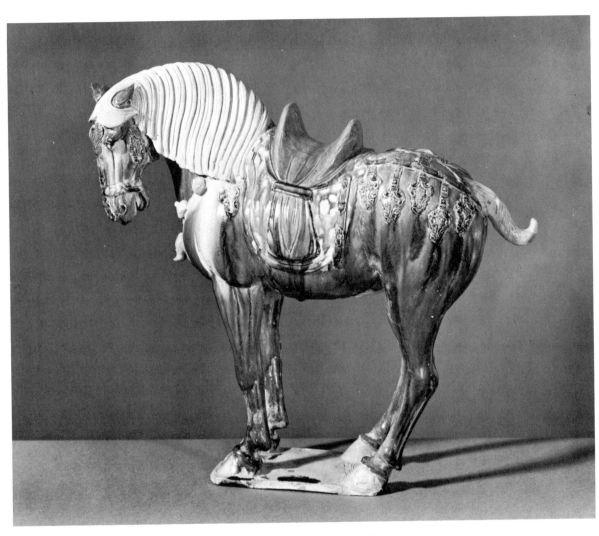

132. *Horse*. Chinese, T'ang dynasty. Lent by Mr. and Mrs. James Biddle.

133. *Celestial Dancer*.
Chinese, Sung dynasty.
Lent by Mr. and Mrs. James Biddle.

134. *Jar*.
Japanese, Jomon period,
3rd millennium B.C.
Lent by Mr. Stuart C. Welch, Jr.

135. *Porcelain Jar.*
Japanese, Edo period,
last quarter of 17th century.
Lent by Mr. Henry F. Harrison.

136. *Pied Wagtail on a Lotus Frond.* Chinese, Yüan dynasty.
Lent by Mr. Benjamin Rowland, Jr.

137. *Seishi Bosatsu.* Japanese,
Late Heian period.
Lent by Mr. Benjamin Rowland, Jr.

138. Sakai Hoitsu.
Flowers in Moonlight.
Japanese, late 18th-early 19th century.
Lent by Mr. Henry F. Harrison.

139. Kitao Masanobu.
Woman under Snowy Willow. Japanese, late 18th century.
Lent by Mr. Henry F. Harrison.

PHOTOGRAPHIC CREDITS

The Asia Society, New York (114, 115) ; E. Irving Blomstrann, New Britain, Conn. (56) ; Brenwasser, New York (32, 62, 93, 94) ; Henry D. Childs, Stow, Mass. (63) ; G. M. Cushing, Boston (57, 64) ; E. R. Deats, Philadelphia (54) ; Helga Photo Studios, Inc., New York (53a-d, 126) ; Michael Katz, New York (91) ; Mathias Komor, New York (127 , 135) ; Paulus Leeser, New York (18, 26, 27, 31a-b, 51, 52, 102a-f) ; Edward Meneeley, New York (80, 84) ; Sydney W. Newbery, London (40, 48) ; Perls Galleries, New York (76) ; Philadelphia Museum of Art (75, 96) ; Eric Pollitzer, New York (97, 99) ; Nathan Rabin, New York (4, 5) ; Taylor and Dull, New York (23, 38, 41, 44, 45, 47, 50, 79, 81, 82, 83, 89, 100, 132, 133) ; Town and Country Studio, Greenwich, Conn. (78) ; Herbert P. Vose, Wellesley Hills, Mass. (58) ; Christopher Whitney, Boston (8, 10, 11, 17, 22, 73, 120, 122, 124, 130, 131, 134) ; Dietrich Widmer, Basel (3, 6, 9, 12, 14) ; Alfred J. Wyatt (118).

Catalogue designed by Gerald Brian Doe
Printed by Triton Press, New York City